COOKING SKINNY
With Edita

Lose Up To 1 Pound A Day & Up To 1 Pound Overnight by....

COOKING SKINNY
with Edita

Over 200 Recipes
Over 130 Food Tips
Easy. Economical. Fun.
Edita's Skinny AM-PM System
AM Foods To Block Fat All Day
Breakfasts, Lunches & Morning Snacks
PM Foods To Burn Fat All Night
Dinners, Desserts & Bedtime Snacks
2-Day Weekend Fast Fat Loss Menu
5-Day Fat Detox Menu
Skinny Supplements That Work In Seconds

By

Edita Kaye

Copyright 2003 by Fountain of Youth Group, LLC
All rights reserved.

Fountain of Youth Group, LLC
830-13 A1A North
Ponte Vedra Beach, FL 32082
Call toll free 1-888-7-SKINNY
www.skinny.com or www.editakaye.com

Printed in the United States of America
First printing.

Published by:
Fountain of Youth Group, LLC
830-13 A1A North
Ponte Vedra Beach, FL 32082

ISBN 0-9635150-6-3

Library of Congress Cataloging-in-Publication Data
Kaye, Edita
Cooking Skinny with Edita:/Edita Kaye
1. Weight Loss 2. Diet 3. Nutrition 4. Food 5. Cooking

Other Books by Edita Kaye

Skinny Rules
The Skinny Pill
The Fountain of Youth
Bone Builders

Testimonials From Edita's Skinny Stars

I had fat deposits on my arms and legs and they are significantly reduced. I'm telling all my friends that Edita's Skinny System is great. *Sue A., Tennessee.*

I lost 40 pounds in just over a month. This was easy. *Richard F., California.*

I lost 32 pounds in four months. I love this whole system of Edita's. *Patricia F., New Jersey.*

I lost 6 pounds in 6 days. It's the fastest program I've ever seen. *Maria S., Pennsylvania.*

It's only been nine days, but people are already asking me what diet I'm on and how much I've lost because my clothes are beginning to hang on me and my weight loss is noticeable. *Daniel W., Ohio.*

I lost 10 pounds in the first 5 days. I stood on my scale and almost cried from joy. *Jennifer A., Florida.*

My husband and I started Monday and by Thursday we had lost 9 pounds. *Donna E., Arizona.*

I lost 61 pounds in just 15 weeks and I have kept it off for six months. And since I love to cook and its so hard to find recipes that help you lose, I'm loving this. *Sheila T., Michigan.*

I lost 25 pounds and I think your program has made all the difference. *Sandy W, Oklahoma*

I lost 48 pounds in less than six months. I love Edita's Skinny System and so does my doctor. *Carol D., Minnesota*

I lost 10 pounds in a week! *Stacy T., Texas*

I was having a hard time losing the few pounds I wanted to lose. Edita's book really showed me "how" to eat. I lost 10 pounds in the first 14 days. This is one program that really works. I'm going to keep ordering and taking the pills and following Edita's System just to maintain where I am at this point. *Shelley M., Colorado*

I lost 70 pounds and my husband has lost 25 pounds. I've already told ten friends about this wonderful Skinny System. *Lynn K., Illinois.*

I lost 40 pounds and my husband lost 30 pounds. We celebrated by booking a cruise! *Sharon N., Florida.*

When I started on the Skinny System I weighed 210 pounds. Now, just a few weeks later, I'm down to 170 pounds. This program and the Skinny Pills are the first diet products that really worked. *John J., Pennsylvania.*

Edita's Skinny Pills and Skinny Foods work! I've told everyone at work to start this system, right away. *Susan P., New York.*

Welcome to COOKING SKINNY *with Edita*

I'm so excited that you have decided to start COOKING SKINNY *with Edita*! With me! You are going to have such a good time! You and your whole family are going to enjoy every single one of these delicious recipes. And best of all, you are going to get skinnier and healthier with every bite!

How much will you lose? You could lose as much as 7,000 calories in a 24 hour period. That's 2 fat pounds a day! That's a full dress size every week! Thousands have already lost millions of pounds that fast with my Skinny AM-PM System™, and kept those fat pounds off!

Why did I write this cookbook? Simple. Hundreds of thousands of my satisfied and successful clients and customers asked for more recipes. They wanted to cook skinny and eat skinny every day. And they wanted to make my Skinny AM-PM System an integral part of their lives and the lives of their loved ones.

And so, here you all are. My first cookbook designed especially to fit my Skinny AM-PM System.

Eat. Enjoy. Live well. Be Skinny.

God bless and keep you all.

Edita

Table of Contents

Afternoon Snacks (PM Fat Burners)

Bedtime Snacks (PM Fat Burners)

Desserts (Plus Skinny Carbs ANYTIME Formula)

Resources

Information   **253**

Part One: The System

Edita's Skinny AM-PM System

Whether you are an old friend, getting skinnier and skinnier with me, or whether you are a new friend, trying my Skinny AM-PM System you will start getting skinny in seconds, safely and effectively.

How much will you lose? You could lose from 3 to 14 pounds per week. How fast will you lose? You'll start to lose within seconds of beginning my Skinny System. You'll lose fast. One to two pounds in 24 hours and then one to two pounds every 24 hours for the first 30 to 90 days depending on the amount of fat you need to lose and your own unique body and health situation. How easy is it to lose? Losing fat as easy as telling time. Here's how.

IF YOU CAN TELL TIME, YOU CAN GET SKINNY!

There are two skinny food groups.
1. The AM Food Group is made up of fiber and carbs and it blocks new fat from entering your fat cells.
2. The PM Food Group is made up of protein and it burns and melts away the old fat already stored in your fat cells.

There are three kinds of skinny pills.
They are safe. They are free of ephedra and other dangerous stimulants. And they work.
1. Skinny Pill™ AM—helps get you skinny all day.
2. Skinny Sleep™ Pill PM—helps get you skinny all night.
3. Skinny Carbs™ Pill ANYTIME—helps keep you skinny even when you overindulge. I call it my "Oops I have to cheat" Pill.

Skinny Foods

Skinny Food Group 1: AM Fat Blocker Foods

Fat blocker foods are high in fiber and complex carbohydrates and are eaten when your watch says AM. By eating fat blocking foods first thing in the morning and then throughout the early or AM part of the day, several things happen. You reduce the insulin spikes that lead to fat storage and obesity. You lay down a protective coating that blocks the absorption of any new fat you might ingest from entering fat cells, you begin to scrub out vascular lipids, and you slow down the rate at which your stomach empties, keeping your feeling of fullness and satisfaction lasting longer and preventing cravings and hunger pangs.

Fiber belongs to a branch of the carbohydrate family and is the part that is not digested, but passes right through our system and is excreted. Fiber has no calories. It doesn't add to the dietary calories we can store as fat.

Fiber doesn't break down in our digestive system, which means it can't be absorbed, so again, it can't add to our fat supply. Fiber helps us feel full, soothing our appetite triggering center so that we are better able to refrain from stuffing ourselves. Fiber blocks the absorption of dietary fat –and fat calories—in our intestines and moves it harmlessly through our digestive system and out as waste. Fiber, as new research is showing every day, can help lower our blood fat, reducing cholesterol levels and improving our vascular health. It has also been shown to have a positive effect in reducing our risk for certain cancers and diabetes. Finally, most of us don't get nearly enough fiber every day—only 10 to 15 grams—as opposed to the 25 to 30 grams nutritional experts believe is the ideal and healthy amount.

There are two types of fiber and both are needed to get skinny, fast.

Soluble Fiber: Think Gum

This is the fiber that dissolves in water, becoming sticky and gummy. It's the stickiness that attracts blood fat and cholesterol, pushing it out through your digestive system so it doesn't have a chance to be stored as fat. This is the fiber you think of when you think apples, oranges, broccoli, carrots, and potatoes. As it enters and passes through your system this soluble fiber helps lower cholesterol, reduces your risk for heart disease, improves blood sugar readings and in many cases helps lower blood pressure.

Insoluble Fiber: Think Sponge

This is the fiber you think of when you think of bran muffins, oat bran cereal, oatmeal or popcorn. When you eat this type of fiber and follow it with a big glass of water, the fiber swells up—like a sponge—absorbing the water. The now soft and spongy fiber pushes on and out through your intestines, carrying with it excess dietary fat. As it passes through you, studies show that it helps in your overall digestion, aids elimination, promotes regularity and helps keep bowels clean.

Best AM Fat Blocking Foods

Breads	Oatmeal	Dried Fruit	Beans
Waffles	Oatmeal cookies	Grapefruit	Pasta
Pancakes	Raisins	Peas	White Rice

Apples	Tortillas	Cereal	Brown Rice
Oranges	Bran cereals	Potatoes	Pineapple
Pears	Popcorn	Raspberries	Kiwi
Pretzel	Blueberries	Lentils	Waffles
Pancakes	Bagels	Corn	Grits

Skinny Food Group 2: PM Fat Burner Foods

Fat burner foods are foods high in protein, a thermic element that actually burns or melts fat by raising the body's metabolic rate. By eating thermic foods—foods that produce heat—hot calorie foods—you can burn off 15 percent of your daily calories just in the caloric energy you use to eat, digest and most importantly, process thermic foods. Your metabolic rate increases when you eat these foods because your body has to work very hard to break down and absorb the nutrients in these foods. This produces more heat. More calories are burned off. Fewer calories are available to be stored as fat. This process is called the thermic effect of food. The best thermic foods are those high in protein. By enjoying these foods in the afternoon and evening—during the PM hours of the day—our body can burn fat, while we are more sedentary and even overnight while we sleep. Allowing our own metabolic process to become the ultimate fat fighting instrument.

But not all foods produce the same thermic burn. Not all foods have fat burning hot calories. The best foods are protein-rich foods.

We can increase our metabolic rate through a diet high in thermic foods. Yes, we can actually burn more calories WHILE WE EAT! Look at it this way. Our own body is our best fat burning machine. Just at rest, doing nothing more strenuous than keeping us breathing and blinking our body uses up to 60 percent of the calories we consume. Any amount of physical exercise we do uses up another 25 percent of our calories. That leaves 15 percent. Increase the thermic foods, and you increase the number of calories burned off and reduce your body fat.

Activity	*% of Calories Burned Off*
Resting metabolic rate	60%
Physical exercise	25%
THERMIC FOODS	15%

Best PM Fat Burning Foods

Lean red meat	Pork	Low fat yogurt
Chicken	Turkey	Eggs
Lamb	Fish	Skim milk
Tofu	Cheese	Tofu

Skinny Supplements

NOTE: Whether you select the supplement formulas I have prepared under my own "Skinny" brand, or whether you go to your favorite health food or vitamin store and create your own do-it-yourself supplement formulas to fight obesity, here are my picks--ingredients recommended to help you in your fat fight, safely and without dangerous stimulants.

Why Skinny Supplements?

Good question! Why do we need supplements to help us get skinny in the first place? We need supplements because we often simply don't get enough of the special nutrients our own body needs to help food turn into energy and not get stored as fat. Just as we need calcium supplements, for example, to help our body build and retain bone mass, no matter how much milk, cheese or broccoli we eat, we also need supplements to help us metabolize food in the most efficient and effective way.

But, just as we need a diet rich in calcium—calcium supplements alone just aren't enough, so we need a diet rich in skinny foods—skinny supplements alone aren't enough, either. So enjoy your skinny foods. Take your skinny supplements and enjoy more energy, definition, and health.

SKINNY PILL-AM-DAYTIME

My Skinny Pill AM keeps you skinny all day long from breakfast to bedtime. With an excellent and safe formula of five of the top fat fighting skinny supplements. These supplements start to work in seconds and give you fat fighting energy you can feel.

Carnitine helps burn off stored fat and increases energy.

Chromium is a thermogenic agent, reducing body fat without traditional dieting or exercise. It is an insulin cofactor, helping your body regulate sugar and blood fat more efficiently.

Garcinia Cambogia contains HCA-a compound similar to citric acid. Preliminary research indicates that HCA decreases fat gain by inhibiting lipogenesis, the metabolic process by which our bodies turn food into fat.

Chitosan is a fiber derived from the skeletons of shell fish. It fights fat absorption in two ways. It acts as a fat sponge, absorbing 4 times its own weight in dietary fat. Chitosan also acts like a "plastic wrap" wrapping its fiber strands around dietary fat molecules and preventing them from being absorbed and stored as cellular body fat.

Citrus Aurantium is believed by researchers to have the ability to zero in on special Beta-3 receptors only to trigger their powerful fat fighting signal, without stimulating the receptors that change heart rate or blood pressure. This is fat fighting at its stimulant-free best.

Calcium is now also believed to play an important role in fat metabolism as well in the prevention of many types of cancers. It is widely known that Americans do not get enough calcium daily from their diet and so a recommended daily allowance of 800 mg to 1200 mg is recommended depending on age.

SKINNY SLEEP PILL-PM-NIGHTIME

My Skinny Sleep PM Pill works overnight, and all night long from bedtime to breakfast to help make you skinny, gently, safely, while you sleep so you can wake up skinnier than when you went to bed.

New research now indicates that possibly one of the major causes of obesity is fatigue. We simply don't get enough sleep. We often have trouble falling asleep. We wake up frequently during the night. We can't go back to sleep. The result? We are overtired and we try to gain back the energy we need through fast-energy foods. The problem is, these foods are high in simple sugars and add extra fat pounds and inches with every bite.

An overnight skinny supplement formula should contain two kinds of ingredients—those that promote an anxiety-free, restful and deep sleep and those that keep our metabolism melting fat all night long safely. The result of taking such a formula? You'll wake up rested. You won't immediately crave fast energy foods. You'll wake up skinnier than when you went to bed.

Lipotropic Blend which includes carnitine to help burn off stored fat.

Chromium is a thermogenic agent, reducing body fat without traditional dieting or exercise. It is an insulin cofactor, helping your body regulate sugar and blood fat more efficiently.

Garcinia Cambogia contains HCA-a compound similar to citric acid. Preliminary research indicates that HCA decreases fat gain by inhibiting lipogenesis, the metabolic process by which our bodies turn food into fat.

Citrus Aurantium is believed by researchers to have the ability to zero in on special Beta-3 receptors only to trigger their powerful fat fighting signal, without stimulating the receptors that change heart rate or blood pressure. This is fat fighting at its stimulant-free best.

Sleep and Fatigue Fighters include chamomile and melatonin which help keep our bodies "in sync", rested, relaxed and anxiety-free.

SKINNY CARBS PILL-ANYTIME

My Skinny Carbs Pill blocks extra fat-making starches and carbs and are designed to be taken before for those "oops, I have to cheat," situations when you just can't avoid fat, sugar, starch or carbs but don't want to pay the penalty in extra fat pounds.

Chromium plays an important role in the regulation of insulin and glucose levels, curbs cravings and hunger, and helps regulate the metabolic rate. Chromium also promotes loss of body fat and aids in the retention of lean muscle, important to the body's fat burning system.

Vanadium it is believed by researchers, may function in cholesterol, hormone and sugar metabolism. New research has focused on its role in improving insulin action and reducing sugar.

Glucosol has been effectively shown to reduce blood sugar levels. The importance of its relationship to weight control is that the body usually converts excess sugar to stored body fat.

Phaseolus vulgaris (phaseolamine) is an ingredient which has been shown to effectively prevent the body from absorbing up to 35 grams of unwanted starch per meal. It is found in white kidney beans.

This is my Skinny AM-PM System. Enjoy the foods. Take the pills. And you'll be able to lose up to 2 pounds of fat in every twenty-four hour period—day and night! You'll be able to lose up to a full size every 3 to 5 days! What's more, you'll be able to keep it off, like the thousands who have already succeeded and are now my Skinny Stars!

About COOKING SKINNY *with Edita*

1. Do these recipes fit Edita's Skinny AM-PM System?

Yes. Every one of these recipes has been specially developed to work with Edita's Skinny System, which is very simple, balanced and effective. You will find that the recipes are designed so that you eat foods high in fat blocking fiber and complex carbs in the AM and then the recipes switch giving you lots of fat burning protein in the PM.

2. What exactly is Edita's Skinny AM-PM System?

Remember, everything about Edita's Skinny AM-PM System is based on the clock. If your watch says it's AM you will eat fat-blocking AM foods. AM foods are high in fiber and complex carbs. When your watch switches to PM, you will switch to fat-burning PM foods. PM foods are high in fat burning protein. That's it. It's that simple.

3. How does the Breakfast (AM Fat Blocker) work?

You'll see that all breakfasts are marked AM Fat Blocker Breakfast. That means they are high in fiber and complex carbs and will help block any new fat from sticking. These breakfasts help keep you from getting any fatter.

4. In *The Skinny Pill* book Edita has a Pre-Breakfast, and yet, there are no pre-breakfasts listed in the recipes. Why is that? What should I do about pre-breakfast?

Edita's pre-breakfast is always the same—an orange, an apple, or any other high fiber fresh fruit. No recipe can improve on that formula. It's the best way to begin your skinny day—every day! Remember, orange juice, America's traditional morning start is too high in fat-making sugar. Whole fruit, high in fruit fiber is a much better, skinnier choice.

5. How does the Morning Snack (AM Fat Blocker) work?

The Morning Fat Blocker AM Snack is designed according the International Saity Index (Fullness Index) to reduce hunger by slowing the rate of stomach emptying and calming cravings while the high fiber content blocks fat absorption and helps scrub out vascular lipids.

6. Why are there two lunch selections, a Fat Blocker Lunch and a Fat Burner Lunch? What's the difference between them, and which one should I pick?

If you have LESS than 30 pounds to lose or are at your ideal weight and would like to stay there, you may select a Fat Blocker Lunch. This lunch gives you more fiber and more carbs and helps to block the absorption of new fat. But, if you have MORE than 30 pounds to lose, or are in a hurry to reach your goal, and want to see more fat loss, faster, you should pick the Fat Burner Lunch. You'll get more fat-burning protein power.

7. How does the Afternoon Snack (PM Fat Burner) work?

It is important to eat several times a day. Edita's Skinny AM-PM System takes the importance of multiple meals for insulin regulation into account and encourages a metabolic boosting higher protein meal in the long hours between lunch and dinner.

8. How does Dinner (PM Fat Burner) work?

You'll see that all the dinners are marked Fat Burner Dinner. That means they are high in protein to help burn off already stored fat, faster and give you more energy. These dinners are thermic, and get the fat burning off right away, and keep it burning off all evening long.

9. What can I have with Dinner?

You may have vegetables and salad, but no complex carbs or starchy foods. That lets out things like, pasta, corn, potatoes, peas, beans (except green beans). But it gives you lots of choices like lettuce, tomatoes, peppers, onions, broccoli, cauliflower, cucumbers, and more...

10. How does the Bedtime Snack (PM Fat Burner) work?

You can help your body keep burning fat all night long while you sleep by enjoying a high protein bedtime snack. This snack also helps curb cravings and helps achieve a restful sleep.

11. Can I mix AM and PM meals?

No. If a meal or recipe is marked AM that is the time you may have that meal. If a meal is marked PM that is the time you may have that meal. But, you may select AM meals from different categories. For example, you may have an AM Fat Blocker Breakfast as a Morning Fat Blocker or you might switch a PM Afternoon Snack and a Bedtime Snack, since both are PM fat burners.

12. What about drinks and condiments?

Water, coffee, tea, diet sodas, and beef, chicken or vegetable broth are permitted. No fruit juices are permitted, because of their high fat-making sugar content. You may have mustard, salsa, horseradish and hot sauce with your meals. In fact, these condiments are highly encouraged, because they actually increase your own body's thermic temperature, helping you to burn more fat, faster. You may enjoy the recommended serving of reduced fat or fat free salad dressings, such as mayonnaise, sour cream, and others.

13. Why is there no analysis of recipes, including calories, fat content, carbohydrate content, protein, sodium, etc?

Because I have done the counting, measuring, worrying for you. All you have to do is eat, enjoy and get skinny!

14. What about Skinny Supplements? Do I need them?

You can get skinny by following my Skinny AM-PM System and eating skinny foods as outlined. However, my Skinny Supplement Formulas—Skinny Pills will help you to lose faster and more effectively.

15. What about Dessert?

My desserts have been created to satisfy your sweet tooth, calm your cravings and still be as healthy as possible so as not to add too many fat pounds and inches. I always recommend that you take a couple of my Skinny Carbs before indulging so as to give yourself a little more protection against unwanted deposits of fat.

About Edita's Special Skinny Recipes

I have formulated several special skinny recipes designed to work with my Skinny AM-PM System. I recommend that you use these recipes when you want to really get a quick start on your fat loss program. So, I've put together two special diets or menus to show you how easy it is to get skinny using my system.

You can repeat my 2-Day Fast Fat Loss Menus or my 5-Day Fat Detox Menus for 30-days, 60-days or even 90-days, depending on how much fat you wish to lose, and how quickly you wish to lose it.

Remember, you can always enjoy all my Cooking Skinny with Edita recipes so you don't get bored.

Edita's Special Recipe Skinny Banana Split
(AM Fat Blocker)

1 banana, peeled and split
1 orange, peeled & chopped
1 kiwi fruit, peeled & chopped
½ cup raspberries, blueberries, or strawberries
1 big scoop nonfat frozen yogurt

Arrange the banana on a small plate or dish. Top with the frozen yogurt. Smother with the mixed fruit. Makes one serving.

Edita's Special Recipe Skinny Cookies
(AM Fat Blocker)

½ cup oatmeal
½ cup oat bran
½ cup raisins
1 cup low fat pancake mix
½ cup brown sugar
½ cup unsweetened applesauce
4 to 6 packets artificial sweetener
½ cup water or enough to form cookie consistency.

Preheat oven to 350°F.
Combine all ingredients in a medium bowl. Stir with a fork until well mixed. Drop by teaspoonfuls on a nonstick cookie sheet. Flatten slightly with the back of a fork. Bake 15 minutes or until golden brown. Cool. Store in an airtight container in the fridge. Makes 1 dozen cookies.
Serving size: 2 cookies

A Little Soul Food
Don't curse the darkness. Light a candle.

Edita's Special Recipe Skinny Munchies
(AM Fat Blocker)

3 cups Total® cereal
3 cups hot-air popped popcorn
1 cup mini whole wheat crackers
1 cup lightly salted pretzel sticks
2 tablespoons vegetable oil
½ teaspoon chili powder
¼ teaspoon ground cumin
1 teaspoon garlic powder
2 tablespoons grated Parmesan cheese

Preheat oven to 300°F

Mix cereal, popcorn, crackers and pretzels in a large plastic bag. In a small bowl combine the oil and spices.
Pour over the dry mixture. Shake well. Add the cheese.
Pour into an ungreased rectangular baking pan, 13 x 9 x 2-inches. Bake 10 minutes. Cool. Store in a tightly covered container.

Makes 8 cups.   Serving size: 1 cup

A Little Soul Food
Always do a little more than you think you can.

Edita's Special Recipe Skinny Fruit Salad
(AM Fat Blocker)

1 apple, unpeeled, cored & chopped
1 pear, unpeeled, cored & chopped
1 orange, peeled & chopped
1 cup raspberries, blueberries or strawberries

Combine all fruit in a large bowl. Chill.

Makes 4 servings.   Serving size: 1 cup

Edita's Special Recipe Skinny Veggie Salad
(Anytime)

1 head Romaine lettuce, chopped
1 bunch fresh spinach, chopped
2 bunches scallions, chopped
4 stalks celery, chopped
1 red pepper, seeded & chopped
1 green pepper, seeded & chopped
1 tomato, chopped
1 bunch parsley, chopped

Combine all ingredients in a large plastic container. Store in fridge. Enjoy 2 to 4 cups at a time with your favorite reduced fat salad dressing.

Edita's Special Recipe Skinny Steamed Veggies
(Anytime)

1 large head broccoli, cut into flowerets
1 red pepper, seeded and sliced
1 green pepper, seeded and sliced
1 yellow pepper, seeded and sliced
1 pound green beans
1 large onion, peeled and sliced
3 stalks celery, sliced
1 cup peanuts, pecans or sliced almonds

In a large plastic bag combine the veggies. Seal and keep in the fridge until used. When ready to use, steam veggies until crisp tender. Serve with lemon juice, balsamic vinegar, your favorite reduced fat salad dressing or 1 tablespoon Parmesan cheese. Serving size: Up to two cups

Edita's Special Recipe Skinny Deli Platter
(PM Fat Burner)

3 slices low fat ham or
3 slices low fat turkey or
3 slices low fat chicken
1 ounce low fat cheese
1 hard-boiled egg—white only
1 sliced tomato
2 large leaves Romaine lettuce

Arrange the meats, cheese, egg and tomato on the lettuce leaves. Enjoy! Makes one serving.

Skinny Weekend-2 Day Fast Fat Loss Menu

My special Skinny Weekend Fast Fat Loss Menu is designed to accelerate fat loss and help you lose from 5 to 7 fast fat pounds and one to two sizes, in just two days. This is a great head start for you and your family.

Saturday

Pre-Breakfast (fat-blocker)
One Orange

Breakfast (fat blocker)
2 pancakes or 2 waffles with 2 tablespoons of syrup

Morning Snack (fat blocker)
Edita's Special Recipe Skinny Cookies
Skinny Pill AM

Lunch (fat burner)
Edita's Special Recipe Skinny Veggie Salad

Afternoon Snack (fat burner)
2 stalks celery with 2 tablespoons peanut butter

Dinner (fat burner)
Omelet made with three eggs and Edita's Special Recipe Skinny Salad and Skinny Veggies

Bedtime Snack (fat burner)
Edita's Special Recipe Skinny Deli Platter
Skinny Sleep Pill PM

Sunday

Pre-Breakfast (fat blocker)
One Orange

Breakfast (fat blocker)
Edita's Special Recipe Skinny Banana Split

Morning Snack (fat blocker)
Edita's Special Recipe Skinny Munchies
Skinny Pill AM

Lunch (fat burner)
One individual size can of tuna packed in water with
Edita's Special Recipe Skinny Veggie Salad

Afternoon Snack (fat burner)
3 ounces of your favorite cheese or one individual size
container of your favorite nonfat yogurt

Dinner (fat burner)
A 6-ounce steak, or one chicken breast without skin,
broiled or a 6-ounce salmon steak, broiled or poached and
Edita's Special Recipe Skinny Veggie Salad and Edita's
Special Recipe Steamed Veggies

Bedtime Snack (fat burner)
Edita's Special Recipe Skinny Deli Platter
Skinny Sleep Pill PM

Skinny Week-5 Day Fat Detox Diet

Day 1-Fat Detox

Pre-Breakfast (fat blocker)
One orange, apple, or pear

Breakfast (fat blocker)
1 cup oatmeal with 2 teaspoons brown sugar.

Morning Snack (fat blocker)
Edita's Special Recipe Skinny Cookies
Skinny Pill AM

Lunch (fat burner)
Individual can water-packed tuna and Edita's Special
Recipe Skinny Veggie Salad.

Afternoon Snack (fat burner)
½ cantaloupe or ½ honey dew melon or 1 cup watermelon

Dinner (fat burner)
8 ounces steak, broiled or 2 veggie burger patties and
Edita's Special Recipe Skinny Veggie Salad and Edita's
Special Skinny Steamed Veggies

Bedtime Snack (fat burner)
Edita's Special Recipe Skinny Deli Platter
Skinny Sleep Pill PM

Day 2-Fat Detox

Pre-Breakfast (fat blocker)
One orange, apple or pear

Breakfast (fat blocker)
One bagel or English muffin with 1 teaspoon jam, or jelly

Morning Snack (fat blocker)
Edita's Special Recipe Skinny Munchies
Skinny Pill AM

Lunch (fat blocker)
1 cup lentil or pea soup with 1 small bagel and Edita's
Special Recipe Skinny Veggie Salad

Afternoon Snack (fat burner)
3 ounces of cheese

Dinner (fat burner)
8 ounces broiled or poached fish or 2 scrambled eggs with
one slice of ham or two slices of bacon and Edita's Special
Recipe Skinny Veggie Salad and Skinny Steamed Veggies

Bedtime Snack (fat burner)
Edita's Special Recipe Skinny Deli Platter
Skinny Sleep Pill PM

Day 3-Fat Detox

Pre-Breakfast (fat blocker)
One orange, apple or pear

Breakfast (fat blocker)
1 cup Total® cereal with ½ cup skim milk and ½ cup
raisins or 1 small bran muffin with 2 teaspoons jam or jelly

Morning Snack (fat blocker)
Edita's Special Recipe Skinny Fruit Salad
Skinny Pill AM

Lunch (fat burner)
2 hamburger patties, broiled and Edita's Special Recipe
Skinny Veggie Salad

Afternoon Snack (fat burner)
2 stalks of celery with 1 tablespoon peanut butter.

Dinner (fat burner)
8 ounces steak, broiled or 2 veggie burger patties and
Edita's Special Recipe Skinny Veggie Salad and Edita's
Special Recipe Skinny Steamed Veggies

Bedtime Snack (fat burner)
Edita's Special Recipe Skinny Deli Platter
Skinny Sleep Pill PM

Day 4-Fat Detox

Pre-Breakfast (fat blocker)
One orange, apple or pear

Breakfast (fat blocker)
2 slices of whole grain toast with two teaspoons of jam or jelly or 1 bran muffin

Morning Snack (fat blocker)
Edita's Special Recipe Skinny Cookies
Skinny Pill AM

Lunch (fat burner)
4 slices turkey or a small individual can of water packed tuna and Edita's Special Recipe Skinny Veggie Salad

Afternoon Snack (fat burner)
3 ounces cheese

Dinner (fat burner)
8 ounces of fish, broiled or poached and Edita's Special Recipe Skinny Veggie Salad and Skinny Steamed Veggies

Bedtime Snack (fat burner)
Edita's Special Recipe Skinny Deli Platter
Skinny Sleep Pill PM

Day 5-Fat Detox

Pre-Breakfast (fat blocker)
One orange, apple, or pear

Breakfast (fat blocker)
2 waffles or 2 pancakes or one scone with 2 teaspoons jam or jelly

Morning Snack (fat blocker)
Edita's Special Recipe Skinny Munchies or Edita's Special Recipe Skinny Fruit Salad
Skinny Pill AM

Lunch (fat blocker)
1 baked potato topped with either Edita's Special Recipe Veggie Salad or Steamed Veggies

Afternoon Snack (fat burner)
½ cup peanuts or cashews

Dinner (fat burner)
8 ounces veal, pork, or lamb, veggie burger patties or fish baked, broiled or grilled with Edita's Special Recipe Skinny Veggie Salad and Skinny Steamed Veggies

Bedtime Snack (fat burner)
Edita' Special Recipe Skinny Deli Platter
Skinny Sleep Pill PM

Part Two: The Cookbook

Twice the Berry Muffins
(AM Fat Blocker)

1 ½ cups flour
½ cup cream of wheat cereal, uncooked
½ artificial sweetener
1 tablespoon baking powder
1 teaspoon ground cinnamon
1 container (8-ounces) raspberry non-fat yogurt
1 cup egg substitute
¼ cup skim milk
¾ cup fresh blueberries
cooking spray

Preheat oven to 400°F.
1. Mix flour, cereal, sweetener, baking powder and cinnamon; set aside. Blend yogurt, egg substitute, and milk until well blended. Stir into dry ingredients just until blended; stir in blueberries.
2. Line muffin tins with paper muffin cups. Fill cups ¾ full. Bake 20 minutes or until done.

Makes 12 servings.   Serving size: 1 muffin

Edita's Tip
*Blueberries are now recognized as one of
the richest source of antioxidants to keep you
young, healthy and skinny!*

Breakfast Brownies
(AM Fat Blocker)

¾ cup pastry flour
1 teaspoon baking powder
¼ teaspoon salt
½ cup mashed tofu
2 tablespoons applesauce
2 tablespoons honey
1/3 cup maple syrup
1 teaspoon vanilla
¼ cup unsweetened carob powder
cooking spray

Preheat oven to 350°F.

1. Combine all dry ingredients and wet ingredients in separate bowls. Mix together well with mixer until very smooth. If too thick, add 1 tablespoon of water.
2. Spread batter in an 8-inch non-stick square pan sprayed lightly with cooking spray. Bake 20-25 minutes or until a toothpick comes out clean. Do not over bake! Let cool about 10 minutes. Cut into squares.

Makes 16 servings.   Serving size: 1 brownie

Edita's Tip
This recipe was the very first one I made with tofu.
It won me over!

Orange Raisin French Toast
(AM Fat Blocker)

2 eggs, lightly beaten
1 cup skim milk
2 teaspoons orange zest (grated orange rind)
8 slices raisin bread
cooking spray

1. In a shallow bowl combine the eggs, milk and orange zest.
2. Dip the slices into the mixture one at a time, both sides until they are well coated.
3. Fry in a large skillet sprayed with non fat cooking spray until both sides are golden brown. Serve hot with a little maple syrup or a light dusting of powdered sugar.

Makes 4 servings.   Serving size: 2 slices

Morning Rice Pudding
(AM Fat Blocker)

1 cup of cooked brown or white rice
½ cup skim milk or soy milk
Handful of raisins
½ teaspoon vanilla
2 teaspoons honey

Put all ingredients in bowl and stir. Microwave 2 minutes, and eat! Makes 1 serving.

Ultimate Breakfast Parfait
(AM Fat Blocker)

2 cups plain nonfat yogurt
2 cups of your favorite granola without nuts
2 cups fresh berries hulled and sliced (raspberries,
blueberries, strawberries)
4 tablespoons honey

1. Spoon 2 tablespoons of yogurt into each glass and smooth surface.
2. Spoon 2 tablespoons of granola overtop and smooth surface.
3. Spoon 2 tablespoons of fruit overtop and smooth surface.

Repeat the process, adding a bit of honey here and there to taste.

Makes 4 servings.

Edita's Tip
Put out the ingredients for this
wonderful breakfast dessert, and let your
family make their own any way they like!

Pear Muffins
(AM Fat Blocker)

3 cups all-purpose flour
2 cups sugar
2 teaspoons ground cinnamon
2 eggs
½ cup vegetable oil
½ cup applesauce
1 teaspoon vanilla extract
6 ripe pears, peeled, seeded and chopped

Preheat oven to 350°F.
1. In a large mixing bowl combine the flour, sugar, baking soda and cinnamon.
2. In another bowl, combine the eggs, oil, applesauce and vanilla. Stir into the flour mixture. Fold in the pears.
3. Pour into paper-lined muffin cups, two-thirds full and bake for 25 to 30 minutes or until a toothpick comes out clean. Cool slightly on wire rack.

Makes 24 muffins.   Serving size: 1 muffin

Edita's Tip
It's so hard to find fun recipes using pears. These are great. And if you have any leftover pears, just use them as a morning snack.

Green Onion Hash
(AM Fat Blocker)

2 leftover baked potatoes
1 tablespoon olive oil
5 scallions, finely chopped, whites and greens
Salt and pepper or steak seasoning blend

1. Scoop cooked potatoes from shells and coarsely chop. Heat a medium non-stick skillet over medium heat. Add oil to pan.
2. Add green onions, and cook one minute. Add potatoes and cook, turning occasionally, until potatoes are crusted and golden and onions begin to brown at edges. Salt and pepper to taste.

Makes 4 servings.

Edita's Tip
I LOVE potatoes for breakfast!

Apple Crisp
(AM Fat Blocker)

4 apples, cored and sliced
4 tablespoons brown sugar
8 tablespoons quick-cooking oats
8 tablespoons all-purpose flour
½ teaspoon cinnamon
½ teaspoon nutmeg
4 tablespoons reduced fat margarine

Preheat oven to 350°F.
1. Place the apple in a layer in a nonstick baking dish.
2. In a mixing bowl combine the sugar, oats, flour and spices. Add the margarine and mix with your fingers until it resembles coarse crumbs.
3. Sprinkle the mixture over the fruit. Bake for 15 to 20 minutes or until apples are tender when pierced with a fork.

Makes 4 servings.   Serving size: 1 cup

Edita's Tip
There is nothing so special as knowing you can have dessert for breakfast and still get skinny!

Rainbow Muffins
(AM Fat Blocker)

2 cups all-purpose flour
2/3 cup artificial sweetener
1 ½ teaspoons baking powder
½ teaspoon baking soda
¼ teaspoon salt
1 ¼ cups low-fat buttermilk
¼ cup applesauce
¼ cup dried blueberries
¼ cup dried cranberries
2 teaspoons grated orange rind
1 teaspoon vanilla extract
1 egg white, slightly beaten

Preheat oven to 400°F.
1. Lightly spoon flour into dry measuring cups; level with a knife. Combine flour and next 4 ingredients in a large bowl. Make a well in the center of mixture.
2. Combine buttermilk and next 6 ingredients (buttermilk through egg white) in a bowl; add to flour mixture.
3. Spoon batter into 12 muffin cups lined with paper muffin cups and sprinkle evenly with 1 tablespoon artificial sweetener. Bake for 18 minutes or until lightly browned. Remove muffins and cool on wire rack.

Makes 12 servings.   Serving size: 1 muffin

Breakfast Burritos
(AM Fat Blocker)

4 tablespoons green onions, thinly sliced
2 tablespoon red bell pepper, finely chopped
4 teaspoons fresh cilantro, chopped
¼ teaspoon salt
1/8 teaspoon black pepper
1/2 cup plain tofu
cooking spray
2 (8-inch) fat-free tortilla
4 tablespoons salsa

1. Combine the first 6 ingredients. Place a small non-stick skillet coated with cooking spray over medium-high heat until hot. Add tofu, and cook, without stirring, until it begins to set on the bottom. Draw a spatula across the bottom of pan to form large curds. Continue cooking until tofu is firm but still moist.
2. Place the tortillas on a microwave-safe plate and microwave at high 15 seconds. Top with tofu and salsa, and roll up.

Makes 2 servings.

Edita's Tip
Here's another way to sneak in some tofu and give it a spicy twist!

Sweet Potato Pancakes with Dried Cranberries
(AM Fat Blocker)

1 ¼ cups all-purpose flour
2 ¼ teaspoons baking powder
1 teaspoon pumpkin-pie spice
¼ teaspoon salt
1 cup skim milk
¼ cup packed dark brown sugar
1 tablespoon applesauce
1 teaspoon vanilla extract
2 egg whites, slightly beaten
1 (16-ounce) can sweet potatoes or yams, drained, mashed

1. Lightly spoon flour into dry measuring cup; level with a knife. Combine flour, baking powder, 2 teaspoons dried cranberries, pumpkin-pie spice, and salt in a large bowl. Combine milk and next 4 ingredients (milk through eggs); add to flour mixture, stirring until smooth. Stir in sweet potatoes.
2. Spoon about ¼ cup batter onto a hot nonstick skillet or griddle. Turn pancakes when tops are covered with bubbles and edges look cooked.

Makes 6 servings.

Edita's Tip
Serve these with hot stewed apples or a spoonful of applesauce for a wonderful weekend breakfast or brunch!

Skinny Ambrosia
(AM Fat Blocker)

3 oranges
2 ruby red or pink grapefruit
2 cups strawberry halves
2 kiwifruit, peeled and cut into wedges
¼ cup flaked unsweetened coconut
3 tablespoons brown sugar

1. Peel and section oranges and grapefruit over a bowl;
    squeeze membranes to extract juice. Add sections
    to bowl; discard membranes. Stir in remaining
    ingredients. Cover and chill.
Makes 6 servings.

Breakfast Fruit a la Mode
(AM Fat Blocker)

2 large baking apples, seeded and sliced
1 large orange, peeled, seeded and sliced
1 large ripe pear, seeded and sliced
¼ cup water
¼ cup maple syrup
½ teaspoon cinnamon
1 teaspoon vanilla

1. In a large nonstick skillet combine the fruit, water,
    syrup, vanilla and cinnamon and bring to a boil.
2. Reduce heat. Cover. Simmer for 5 minutes until frut
    is tender. Serve hot with ice cream or frozen yogurt.
Makes 6 servings.   Serving size: 1 cup

Stuffed Baked Apples
(AM Fat Blocker)

4 large baking apples, cored
½ cup raisins
1 orange, peeled, seeded and chopped
2 tablespoons orange zest (grated orange rind)
½ teaspoon cinnamon
1 cup water

Preheat oven to 375°F.
1. Place the apples in a nonstick baking pan.
2. In a bowl mix the raisins, orange, cinammon and zest and fill each apple cavity with the mixture. Drizzle a little water over each apple and pour the remaining water into the bottom of the baking pan.
3. Bake for 20 to 30 minutes, until the apples are tender. Serve hot or cold.

Makes 4 servings.   Serving size: 1 stuffed apple

A Little Soul Food
The soul can split the sky in two and let the face of God shine through.

Apricot Pineapple Surprise
(AM Fat Blocker)

4 (1-inch thick) peeled fresh pineapple slices
2 tablespoons apricot preserves – no sugar added
1 teaspoon artificial sweetener
Dash of ground cinnamon
1 cup vanilla low-fat frozen yogurt

Preheat broiler.
1. Place pineapple slices on a broiler pan. Brush pineapple slices with preserves; broil 6 minutes or until bubbly.
2. Combine sweetener and cinnamon, and sprinkle over pineapple.

Serve warm with one scoop of vanilla low-fat frozen yogurt.

Makes 1 serving.

Edita's Tip
Frozen yogurt for breakfast—divine decadence! You could also try this extraordinary breakfast with fresh strawberries and strawberry jelly, fresh raspberries and raspberry jelly!

Hot Fruit Sundae
(AM Fat Blocker)

½ cup applesauce
1 ½ cups fresh cranberries
½ cup unsweetened cranberry juice
½ cup unsweetened apple cider
¼ cup artificial sweetener
1 (1 inch) lemon rind strip
4 cups sliced peeled golden delicious apples
2 cups firm Anjou pears, cored and cut into ¼ inch
thick wedges
cooking spray
3 cups vanilla low-fat ice cream

Preheat oven to 400°F

1. To drain applesauce, spread onto several layers of heavy-duty paper towels. Cover with additional paper towels; let stand 5 minutes. Scrape into a mixing bowl using a rubber spatula. This drains the applesauce.
2. Combine cranberries, juice, cider, sweetener, and rind in a small saucepan; bring to a simmer, stirring occasionally. Remove from heat. Stir in applesauce.
3. Combine the apple and pears in an 11x17 inch-baking dish coated with cooking spray. Top with the cranberry mixture. Cover and bake for 25 minutes. Uncover and bake an additional 10 minutes or until fruit is tender, basting occasionally with liquid from dish. Serve with ice cream.

Makes: 4 servings

Morning Glory Muffins
(AM Fat Blocker)

2 cups all-purpose flour
2 teaspoons baking powder
1 teaspoon baking soda
½ teaspoon cinnamon
½ teaspoon nutmeg
½ teaspoon mace
1 apple, peeled, cored, and grated
1 carrot, peeled, and grated
1 cup applesauce
½ cup honey
2 eggs
½ cup crushed pineapple, packed in juice, drained

Preheat oven to 350°F
1. In a large mixing bowl, sift together the dry ingredients.
2. Mix together the carrot, apple, oil, honey, until well blended. Add the eggs, one at a time mixing after each addition. Slowly add in the dry ingredients, mixing after each addition. Fold in the pineapple.
3. Spoon into paper muffin cups about ¾ full and bake for 30 to 40 minutes or until a toothpick inserted in the center comes out clean. Cool on wire rack.

Makes 12 muffins   Serving size: 1 muffin

Edita's Tip
While you are whipping up these hum a few bars of
"Morning has broken..." to feed your soul.

Mesa Corn Muffins
(AM Fat Blocker)

¾ cup skim milk
¼ cup plain, nonfat yogurt
3 tablespoons maple syrup
2 eggs
1 cup all-purpose flour
¾ cup cornmeal
½ teaspoon baking soda

Preheat oven to 375°F

1. Mix together the milk, yogurt, maple syrup, and eggs, blending well.
2. In another bowl combine the flour, cornmeal and baking soda and add to the milk mixture, stirring well to blend.
3. Spoon into lined paper muffin cups, about ¾ full and bake for 15 to 20 minutes or until a toothpick inserted in the center comes out clean. Cool slightly on wire rack.

Makes 12 muffins   Serving size: 1 muffin

Edita's Tip
These are great dipped in a little extra maple syrup! Smile.
It's going to be a terrific, skinny day.

Pineapple Oatmeal
(AM Fat Blocker)

1 ½ cups water
1 can (8 ounces) crushed pineapple, in juice un-drained
1 cup quick cooking oats
½ cup raisins
2 tablespoons brown sugar
¼ teaspoon cinnamon

In a microwave-safe bowl, combine the water and crushed pineapple. Microwave on high about 6 minutes or until boiling. Stir in the rest of the ingredients and microwave on high for 30 to 60 seconds or until the mixture begins to thicken. Serve hot. Makes 2 servings.

Maple Syrup Oatmeal
(AM Fat Blocker)

3 ½ cups skim milk
2 cups rolled oats, quick cooking
¼ cup maple syrup
½ cup raisins
1 cup chopped, unpeeled apple

Bring milk to a low boil and stir in oats cooking for about 5 minutes over medium heat, stirring occasionally.
Remove from heat and add maple syrup, raisins, and apple. Mix well. Serve hot. Makes 4 servings.

Pink Breakfast Shake
(AM Fat Blocker)

2 cups low fat strawberry yogurt
2 oranges, peeled and chopped
¼ cup wheat germ
¼ cup honey

Place all ingredients in a blender. Cover. Process for 20 seconds until smooth. Pour into tall glasses. Makes 4 servings.

Edita's Tip
Garnish your glass with a slice of fresh orange or a juicy red strawberry. You are special and worth the effort!

Swiss Mountain Muesli
(AM Fat Blocker)

1 cup instant rolled oats
1 cup plain, nonfat yogurt
1 apple, peeled and shredded
¼ cup raisins

Mix the ingredients together in a bowl. Let sit for 15 minutes. Enjoy. Makes 2 servings.

Edita's Tip
Make this the night before and store it in individual containers in the fridge. Next morning, just grab it and go!

French Toast By The Spoonful
(AM Fat Blocker)

4 slices cinnamon raisin bread, cut into ½-inch cubes
1 egg
1 cup skim milk
1 teaspoon maple syrup
¼ teaspoon cinnamon
cooking spray

1. Mix the egg, milk, maple syrup and cinnamon in the bowl using a whisk.
2. Throw the bread cubes into the mixture and mix to coat well.
3. Pour the mixture into the skillet coated with the cooking spray and cook on medium heat until set about 5 to 10 minutes. Serve hot.

Makes 2 servings.

Edita's Tip
I love this served with a little heated applesauce or sprinkled with a bit of diced, chopped candied ginger!

Cinnamon Toast
(AM Fat Blocker)

8 slices white or raisin bread
2 tablespoons reduced fat margarine, melted
2 tablespoons sugar
1 tablespoon cinnamon

1. In a small bowl, mix together the sugar and cinnamon.
2. Toast the bread.
3. With a pastry brush, brush one side of each toasted slice with the melted margarine and sprinkle lightly with the cinnamon sugar mixture.
4. Broil, topping side up, until the sugar melts.

Makes 4 servings   Serving size: 2 slices

Edita's Tip
This is one of my favorite "comfort food" breakfasts. It's great for those days when you wake up really needing a food hug!

Farm Apple Muffins
(AM Fat Blocker)

1 ¼ cups bran flakes cereal
1 ¼ cups all-purpose flour
¼ cup brown sugar
1 teaspoon ground cinnamon
1 tablespoon baking powder
1 ¼ cups applesauce
1 apple, peeled, cored and chopped

Preheat oven to 375°F.
1. Combine the cereal, flour, sugar, cinnamon and baking powder in a large mixing bowl.
2. Stir in the applesauce, and apple.
3. Spoon the mixture muffin tins lined with paper muffin cups.
4. Bake for 30 to 40 minutes or until a toothpick inserted in the center comes out clean.

Makes 12 muffins.   Serving size: 1 muffin.

Edita's Tip
Split these and fill them with hot applesauce. Great!

Instant Breakfast One
(AM Fat Blocker)

2 cups skim milk
2 oranges, peeled and chopped
¼ cup wheat germ
¼ cup honey

Place all ingredients in a blender. Cover. Process for 20 seconds until smooth. Makes 2 servings.

Edita's Tip
Try this with strawberries, blueberries, raspberries, blackberries, papaya and even mango.

Instant Breakfast Two
(AM Fat Blocker)

2 cups skim milk
½ cup blueberries
1 apple, peeled and chopped
¼ cup wheat germ
¼ cup honey

Place all ingredients in a blender. Process 20 seconds until smooth. Makes 2 servings.

Edita's Tip
Try this same recipe with 1 cup of strawberries, 1 cup of raspberries or a mixture of oranges, grapefruit and a squeeze of lemon.

Sunrise Salad
(AM Fat Blocker)

1 orange, peeled, seeded and cut into chunks
1 can (11 ounces) mandarin orange sections, drained
1 can (8 ounces) pineapple chunks, drained
1 pear, cored, seeded and cut into chunks
1 apple, cored and cut into chunks

Combine the fruit in a large bowl. Serve. Makes 4 servings.

Edita's Tip
Save this breakfast for a cloudy day, it's like eating a bowl of sunshine!

Breakfast-To-Go
(AM Fat Blocker)

4 pita pockets
4 teaspoons jam or jelly
2 oranges, peeled, seeded and chopped
2 apple, peeled, seeded and chopped
½ cup raisins

Spread the jam or jelly inside each pita pocket and stuff each pita with an equal amount of fruit. Microwave on high for 10 to 20 seconds. Makes 4 servings.

Edita's Tip
Take an extra one of these along and have it for your morning fat blocker AM snack. Take a couple extra to share!

Classic Bran Muffins
(AM Fat Blocker)

1 ¼ cups all-purpose flour
½ cup sugar
1 tablespoon baking powder
2 cups bran flake cereal
1 ¼ cups skim milk
1 egg
¼ cup vegetable oil

Preheat oven to 400°F.
1. Line muffin tins with paper muffin cups.
2. In a large bowl stir together flour, sugar, and baking powder. Set aside.
3. In a separate bowl, combine the bran cereal, and milk.
4. Let stand about 5 minutes or until the cereal is softened. Add the egg and oil. Beat well.
5. Add the flour mixture. Stir until just combined.
6. Fill muffin tins. Bake 20 minutes until lightly browned.

Makes 12 muffins.   Serving size: 1 muffin

Edita's Tip
Spread these with your favorite jam,
jelly or preserves.

Syrup Sweetened Corn Muffins
(AM Fat Blocker)

¾ **cup skim milk**
¼ **cup plain, nonfat yogurt**
3 tablespoons maple syrup
2 eggs
1 cup all-purpose flour
¾ **cup cornmeal**
½ **teaspoon baking soda**

Preheat oven to 375°F.
1. Mix together the milk, yogurt, maple syrup, and eggs.
2. Combine the flour, cornmeal and baking soda and add to the milk mixture. Mix well.
3. Spoon into muffin tins sprayed with cooking spray and bake for 15 to 20 minutes or until a toothpick inserted in the center comes out clean. Cool slightly on wire rack.

Makes 12 muffins.   Serving size: 1 muffin

A Little Soul Food
Winning starts with beginning.

Iron Stove Potato Biscuits
(AM Fat Blocker)

½ cup skim milk, hot
2 tablespoons shortening
2 tablespoons sugar
½ cup mashed potatoes, warm
1 teaspoon salt
3 ¼ cups all-purpose flour
1 package dry yeast
¼ cup warm water

Preheat oven to 425°F
1. Mix together the milk, shortening, potatoes, salt and ¼ cup of the flour and set aside until room temperature.
2. Stir in the yeast into the warm water and let stand for 5 minutes until the yeast dissolves.
3. Add the yeast mixture to the milk mixture and beat with an electric mixer until well mixed.
4. Cover with a clean cloth and set aside in a warm place to rise until it is doubled in bulk and is light.
5. Add the remaining flour. Mix again. Cover and set aside again until it again doubles in bulk.
6. Turn out onto a floured surface. Roll out to a thickness of ¼ inch. Using a pastry cutter or glass, cut into 2-inch rounds. Place the rounds on a cookie sheet sprayed with cooking spray. Let rise again, until double. Bake 15 minutes, or until golden.

Makes 1 dozen biscuits.   Serving size: 1 biscuit

Apple Pie Oatmeal
(AM Fat Blocker)

1 apple, cored, peeled, and chopped
2/3 cup rolled oats
1cup skim milk
¼ teaspoon cinnamon
1 teaspoon brown sugar

1. Put the milk, apple and rolled oats into a medium saucepan.
2. Bring to a boil, stirring often.
3. Reduce heat and simmer until the oatmeal thickens, about 5 minutes. Serve topped with cinnamon and brown sugar.

Makes 2 servings.

Edita's Tip
Here is double portion of fat blocking fiber—the apples and the oatmeal.

Morning Cinnamon Loaf
(AM Fat Blocker)

1 ¾ cups all-purpose or whole-wheat flour
½ cup sugar
1 ½ cup pumpkin pie spice
1 teaspoon cinnamon
1 teaspoon baking soda
1 teaspoon baking powder
1 cup canned pumpkin, mashed
½ cup applesauce
2 tablespoons water

Preheat oven to 350°F.
1. Combine the flour, sugar, spice, baking soda and baking powder in a mixing bowl.
2. Add the pumpkin, and applesauce and mix, adding the water until ingredients are moist.
3. Spray a loaf pan with cooking spray and spread the mixture evenly in the pan.
4. Bake for 40 to 45 minutes or until a toothpick inserted in the center comes out clean.
5. Remove the bread from the oven and let it sit for 10 minutes. Invert onto a wire rack. Slice and serve.

Makes 12 servings.

A Little Soul Food
Don't wait for your ship to come in. Swim out to it.

Sweet Simmered Applesauce
(AM Fat Blocker)

6 apples, peeled, cored, and quartered
¼ cup water
1 tablespoon lemon juice
1 teaspoon cinnamon

1. Combine all the ingredients in a saucepan. Bring to a boil.
2. Reduce heat and simmer uncovered, until apples are tender about 20 minutes.
3. Using a potato masher, mash the apples until the right consistency is achieved.

Makes 6 servings.

Edita's Tip
Serve with graham crackers or vanilla wafers or toasted slices of cinnamon bread.

Skinny AM Snack Bars
(AM Fat Blocker)

4 cups Total® cereal
1 cup raisins
½ cup dried figs, chopped
½ cup dried apricots, chopped
¼ cup reduced fat margarine
2 cups miniature marshmallows

1. In a large mixing bowl mix together the cereal and fruit and set aside.
2. Melt the margarine in the saucepan on medium heat and add the marshmallows, stirring until they melt.
3. Pour the melted marshmallows into the fruit mixture and mix until well coated.
4. Press the mixture into the baking pan, spreading it evenly. Chill for 1 hour. Cut into bars.

Makes 24 bars   Serving Size: 1 bar

Edita's Tip
These bars are so much better—and cheaper—than the store-bought bars that cost way too much and don't taste half as good!

Spicy Pumpkin Bread
(AM Fat Blocker)

1 ¾ cups whole-wheat flour
½ cup sugar
1 ½ cup pumpkin pie spice
1 teaspoon baking soda
1 teaspoon baking powder
1 cup canned pumpkin, mashed
½ cup applesauce
2 tablespoons water

Preheat oven to 350°F

1. Combine the flour, sugar, spice, baking soda and baking powder in the mixing bowl. And mix well.
2. Add the pumpkin, and applesauce and mix, adding the water until the ingredients are moist.
3. Coat the loaf pan with cooking spray and spread the mixture evenly in the pan. Bake for 40 to 45 minutes or until a toothpick inserted in the center comes out clean.
4. Remove the bread from the oven. Let sit for 10 minutes. Invert onto a wire rack. Slice and serve.

Makes 16 servings.

Edita's Tip
This tastes great with slices of ripe tomato.

Stuffed Portobello Mushrooms
(AM Fat Blocker)

6 large Portobello mushrooms
1 teaspoon reduced fat margarine, melted
1 teaspoon garlic, minced
¾ cup reduced fat whole grain crackers, crushed
1 red pepper, seeded and chopped fine
¼ cup green onion, or chives, chopped fine
1 tablespoon Dijon-type mustard

Preheat oven to 400°F
1. Broil the mushrooms, 2 minutes per side, under the broiler. Set aside.
2. In a mixing bowl combine the remaining ingredients. Divide the mixture evenly among the mushrooms, topping each one with the mixture. Bake for 8 to 10 minutes.

Makes 6 servings.

Edita's Tip
This is fancy enough to serve at holiday brunch and no one will believe that you're getting skinnier with every single bite!

Cinnamon Raisin Popcorn
(AM Fat Blocker)

1 package of reduced fat microwave popcorn
¼ cup raisins
½ teaspoon cinnamon

Prepare the popcorn according to package directions. Pour into a bowl. Add the raisins and cinnamon. Toss to combine. Makes 1 serving.

Cranberry Popcorn
(AM Fat Blocker)

1 package of reduced fat microwave popcorn
¼ cup cranberries
½ teaspoon nutmeg

Prepare the popcorn according to package directions. Pour into a bowl. Add the cranberries and nutmeg. Toss to combine. Makes 1 serving

Edita's Tip
Divide the popcorn up into smaller plastic baggies and take it to work with you, give it to the kids for lunch, or keep it in the car for snacks. You're getting extra fat blocking fiber in the popcorn and the raisins!

The Very Best Oatmeal Cookies
(AM Fat Blocker)

1 cup applesauce
1 ½ cups brown sugar
2 eggs
½ cup buttermilk
3 cups uncooked oatmeal
1 ¾ cups all-purpose flour
1 teaspoon baking soda
1 teaspoon baking powder
1 teaspoon cinnamon
1 teaspoon nutmeg
1 cup raisins

Preheat oven to 400°F.

1. In a large bowl, mix the applesauce and brown sugar.
2. Stir in the eggs, one at a time.
3. Stir in the buttermilk.
4. Add the remaining ingredients mixing well after each addition.
5. Drop the dough by spoonfuls onto a nonstick baking sheet sprayed with cooking spray. Flatten slightly with the back of a fork. Bake for 8 minutes or until done. Cool on a baking rack.

Makes 72 cookies.   Serving size: 2 cookies

Skinny Me Brownies
(AM Fat Blocker)

2/3 cup sugar
1/3 cup water
3 tablespoons vegetable oil
1 teaspoon vanilla extract
1 egg
½ cup all-purpose flour
1/3 cup uncooked oatmeal
¼ cup cocoa powder
¾ teaspoons baking powder

Preheat oven to 350°F.

1. In a medium bowl, combine the sugar, water, oil, and vanilla extract, mixing well.
2. Stir in the eggs and beat the mixture until smooth.
3. In a separate bowl, mix together the flour oatmeal, cocoa and baking powder and fold into the sugar mixture. Stir until smooth.
4. Pour the batter into an 8-inch square nonstick pan sprayed with cooking spray. Bake for 20-25 minutes, or until a toothpick inserted in the center comes out clean. Cool in the pan. Cut into 16 2-inch squares.

Makes 12 servings.   Serving size: 1 piece

Sweet Potato Wedges
(AM Fat Blocker)

2 sweet potatoes, peeled, sliced lengthwise into wedges
1 teaspoon olive oil
½ teaspoon curry powder
¼ teaspoon each ground cumin, cinnamon, salt and
pepper

Preheat oven to 425°F.
Place all the ingredients in a large plastic bag. Seal and toss until the potatoes are well coated. Place the coated potatoes on a nonstick cookie sheet in a single layer and bake for 20 to 30 minutes until tender. Serve.
Makes 4 servings.

Savory Oven Fries
(AM Fat Blocker)

2 medium baking potatoes, scrubbed, unpeeled
½ teaspoon salt
½ teaspoon pepper
1 teaspoon each garlic powder, chili powder & olive oil

Preheat oven to 425°F.
Slice potatoes into French fries, leaving the peel on and place into a large plastic bag with the remaining ingredients. Toss until well coated. Place on a nonstick cookie sheet in a single layer and bake for 20 minute until golden, turning once. Serve.
Makes 4 servings.

Black Sombrero Bean Dip
(AM Fat Blocker)

1 15-ounce can black beans, rinsed and drained
½ cup nonfat mayonnaise
½ cup nonfat sour cream
4 ounces green chilies, chopped and drained
2 tablespoons fresh cilantro, chopped
1 teaspoon chili powder
½ teaspoon garlic powder
Dash of hot pepper sauce

1. In a medium bowl mash the beans with a fork.
2. Stir in the remaining ingredients until well blended.
   Serve with heated corn chips or toasted pita wedges.
   Makes 8 servings.

Border Bean Dip
(AM Fat Blocker)

1 cup kidney beans, canned and drained
1 onion, chopped
1 teaspoon garlic, minced
1 tablespoon plain, nonfat yogurt
1 teaspoon nonfat mayonnaise
1 green pepper, seeded and chopped
1/8 teaspoon dried mustard powder
1 tablespoon tomato paste

Combine all the ingredients in a blender or food processor.
Blend until smooth. Add salt to taste. Chill.
Makes 4 servings.

Crispy Tortilla Chips
(AM Fat Blocker)

4 corn tortillas
cooking spray

Preheat oven to 400°F.
1. Lightly spray each side of a tortilla with cooking spray. Cut each tortilla in half, and then in half again. Arrange the wedges on a nonstick cookie sheet. Bake for 3 to 5 minutes on each side until wedges are crispy.

Makes 8 servings.

Potato Stick Snacks
(AM Fat Blocker)

4 medium baking potatoes
4 teaspoons vegetable oil
1 teaspoon dry Italian seasoning
½ teaspoon garlic powder
1 teaspoon salt
½ teaspoon pepper

1. Cut potatoes into 2 x ¼ inch strips. In a large nonstick skillet, heat the oil over medium heat. Add the potato strips. Cook for 10 minutes.
2. Add the spices. Cook an additional 10 minutes until lightly brown and tender, stirring frequently. Serve hot.

Makes 8 servings.

Baked Bagel Chips
(AM Fat Blocker)

1 envelope onion soup mix
2 tablespoons melted magarine
1 teaspoon dried oregano
1 teaspoon dried basil
1 teaspoon dried parsley
¼ teaspoon garlic powder
¼ teaspoon salt
¼ teaspoon pepper
4 plain bagels, cut into 1/8 inch slices

Preheat oven to 300°F.

1. In a small bowl combine all the ingredients, except the bagels. Mix until well blended.
2. Using a pastry brush, brush both sides of the bagel slices with the mixture.
3. Arrange the bagel slices on two non-stick cookie sheets in a single layer.
4. Bake for 40 to 45 minutes, until crisp. Store in an airtight container up to 1 week.

Makes 8 servings.

Edita's Tip
You don't have to be a New Yorker to enjoy this snack.
Make enough to share.

Kitchen Garden Pizza
(AM Fat Blocker)

8 ounces lowfat dill-flavored dip
6 whole wheat pita breads
2 cups chopped cooked vegetables, broccoli, carrots, tomatoes, spinach

Spread the dip equally between the pitas. Divide the vegetables equally between the pita breads. Place under broiler for 1-2 minutes until cheese bubbles.
Makes 6 servings.

Chili Cereal Snack Mix
(AM Fat Blocker)

3 cups Cheerios cereal
3 cups corn chips
1 cup unsalted peanuts or cashews
1 cup pretzels
¼ cup margarine, melted
¼ teaspoon chili, onion and garlic powder

Preheat oven to 325°F.
Place the cereal, chips, nuts, and pretzels into a plastic bag. Add the melted margarine and spices. Shake until coated. Spread coated mixture on a nonstick cookie sheet. Bake for 15 minutes, stirring once. Cool. Can be stored in an airtight container. Makes 8 servings.

Hummus Dip
(AM Fat Blocker)

1 can (15-ounces) chick peas (garbanzo beans)
½ cup lemon juice
¼ cup tahini or sesame paste
1 teaspoon garlic, minced
¼ teaspoon cayenne pepper
salt and pepper to taste

1. Drain chick peas and reserve ¼ of the liquid.
2. In a blender or food processor combine the chick peas, lemon juice, and tahini paste. Process until mixture is smooth.
3. Blend in the reserved liquid a teaspoon at a time until the mixture reaches spreading consistency. Add salt and pepper. Spoon into a serving bowl. Sprinkle with cayenne pepper. Serve with baked pita triangles, crackers or raw vegetables for dipping.

Makes 4 servings.

Edita's Tip
Just close your eyes and taste your way to exotic places. Try using slices of icy cucumber or bitter endive leaves to scoop up this wonderful fat blocking snack.

Hot Italian Breadsticks
(AM Fat Blocker)

1 16-ounce package of roll mix
1 teaspoon Italian flavored seasoning
1 cup hot water
1 egg white, lightly beaten
2 tablespoons vegetable oil

1. Make the rolls according to package directions, adding the seasoning, the water, egg white and oil in a large mixing bowl.
2. Combine until moistened. Shape into a large ball.
3. Turn the dough onto a lightly floured surface. Knead for 5 minutes. Cover and let rest for 5 minutes.
4. Roll the dough out into a large rectangle, approximately 16 x 12-inches. Cut the dough crosswise to form 16 strips. Cut each strip in half. Twist each strip 5 or 6 times and place on an nonstick cookie sheet. Cover and let rise in a warm place for 30 minutes or until doubled in size.
5. Bake for 10 to 15 minutes or until golden.

Makes 32 breadsticks.   Serving size: 1 breadstick

Edita's Tip
For a change of pace try sprinkling the dough with dill or rosemary or basil. And these herbs are loaded with antioxidants. Wonderful!

Spiced Fruit Stew
(AM Fat Blocker)

4 apples, cored and chopped
½ cup golden raisins
1 pear, cored and chopped
½ cup apple juice
2 tablespoons lemon juice
1 cinnamon stick
2 oranges, peeled, seeded and diced
1 cup seedless grapes

In a medium saucepan combine the apples, raisins, pear, apple juice, lemon juice and cinnamon. Bring to a boil. Reduce heat. Cover and simmer 30 minutes. Mix in the oranges and grapes. Simmer another 15 minutes. Serve warm or cool. Makes 8 servings.

Edita's Tip
For a real treat top with nonfat whipped topping.
You won't believe getting rid of fat pounds and fat inches is this good!

Dried Fruit Mix
(AM Fat Blocker)

1 cup each raisins, shredded coconut, dried apricots, dried apple slices, dried figs and dried dates

Mix all the ingredients together and store in an airtight container. Makes 12 servings. Serving size: ½ cup

Granola Bars
(AM Fat Blocker)

1 ¼ cups oatmeal, uncooked
¼ cup flour
¼ cup toasted wheat germ
1/3 cup raisins
1/3 cup chopped dates
¼ teaspoon cinnamon
¼ cup honey
2 tablespoons unsweetened applesauce

Preheat oven to 300°F
1. In a large mixing bowl combine all the ingredients, stirring well until mixed thoroughly.
2. Pat the mixture into a 8-inch square nonstick pan.
3. Bake for 18 to 20 minutes or until the top is lightly brown. Cool. Cut into bars.

Makes 12 servings.   Serving size: 1 bar

Edita's Tip
Dunk these into a steaming cup of herbal tea or a cup of flavored coffee.

Fruit Pinwheels
(AM Fat Blocker)

2 ½ cups unbleached all-purpose flour
1 teaspoon baking soda
3 tablespoons sugar
¼ cup vegetable shortening
⅔ cup skim milk
2 ½ cups strawberries, blueberries or raspberries,
mashed or crushed pineapple, packed in juice and
drained
1 tablespoon reduced fat margarine
¼ cup sugar
cooking spray

Preheat oven to 350°F.

1. In a blender or food processor mix together the flour, baking soda, and the 3 tablespoons of sugar. Add the vegetable shortening and milk. Process until smooth.
2. Turn out dough onto a lightly floured surface to ¼ inch thickness.
3. Spread the dough with either the crushed strawberries, blueberries, raspberries or pineapple and sprinkle with a mixture of the ¼ cup sugar and 1 tablespoon reduced fat margarine. Roll the dough jelly roll style.
4. Place on nonstick cookie sheet sprayed with cooking spray and bake 30 to 40 minutes or until cake is done. Cool. Slice and serve.

Makes 12 slices.   Serving size: 1 slice

Chewy Cookies
(AM Fat Blocker)

6 tablespoons margarine
¾ cup light brown sugar
3 tablespoons egg substitute
1 teaspoon vanilla extract
1 cup flour
1 cup oatmeal, uncooked
½ teaspoon baking soda
½ cup raisins
½ cup chopped dried apricots
½ cup chopped dates

Preheat oven to 300°F.

1. In the bowl of a food processor combine the margarine, brown sugar, egg substitute and vanilla extract.
2. Process the ingredients until smooth. In a mixing bowl combine the flour, oats, and baking soda.
3. Add the dry flour mixture to the sugar mixture. Process again until well combined. Stir in the remaining ingredients.
4. Drop the mixture by rounded teaspoonfuls onto a nonstick cookie sheet. Flatten each cookie slightly with the back of a fork.
5. Bake for 15 to 18 minutes or until crisp. Cool in the pan and then transfer to wire racks and cool. May be stored in an airtight container.

Makes 36 cookies.   Serving size: 1 cookie

Popcorn Balls
(AM Fat Blocker)

½ **cup sugar**
¼ **cup margarine**
½ **cup light corn syrup**
½ **teaspoon salt**
8 cups popped corn

1. Heat the sugar, margarine, corn syrup, and salt in a large saucepan or Dutch oven over medium-high heat, stirring constantly.
2. Stir in the popcorn. Keep stirring until the popcorn is well coated.
3. Cool until you can handle without burning your hands. Dip hands into cold water and shape the popcorn mixture into 2 ½ inch balls. Place on waxed paper to cool.

Makes 8 servings.

Edita's Tip
Send this snack to school with your kids and help keep them healthy and skinny, too!

Citrus Kabobs
(AM Fat Blocker)

24 pineapple chunks canned in juice and drained
24 strawberries
24 chunks of orange, peeled and seeded
24 chunks of grapefruit, peeled and seeded
24 red or green grapes
24 jelly beans

Thread all the ingredients alternatively onto 24 wooden 6-inch skewers.

Makes 24 servings.   Serving size: 2 skewers

Edita's Tip
Get inventive. Use your favorite fruit. Substitute gum drops, licorice pieces, or caramels for the jelly beans.

Hearty Macaroni Vegetable Salad
(AM Fat Blocker)

3 cups pre-cooked elbow macaroni
3 medium yellow squash, sliced
1 each red, yellow, orange, green peppers, sliced
1 small red onion
1 can whole baby corn, rinsed and drained
1 medium carrot, thinly sliced
¼ cup white vinegar
2 tablespoons water
2 tablespoons olive oil

1. In large bowl, combine vegetables and macaroni.
2. Combine remaining ingredients in a jar and shake well.
3. Pour over vegetable mixture and refrigerate for 2 hours.

Makes 6 servings.

Edita's Tip
Slip this into your microwave and turn this exciting salad into a hot, satisfying lunch.

Good Fortune Stir-Fry
(AM Fat Blocker)

½ cup pea pods, sliced
½ cup broccoli, sliced
¼ cup green pepper, sliced
¼ cup mushrooms, sliced
¼ cup water chestnuts
¼ cup carrots, sliced
1 cup quick rice
2 tablespoons. cornstarch
½ teaspoon sugar
1 teaspoon low sodium soy sauce
cooking spray

1. Spray non-fat cooking spray in skillet, then add vegetables
2. Meanwhile, combine rice and water and cook, according to package directions in microwave
3. Add remaining ingredients to vegetable mixture; cook approximately 8 minutes

Makes 4 servings.

Edita's Tip
Remember, you can enjoy carbs and fibers—just make sure you enjoy them in the AM hours and not in the PM hours.

Five Bean Salad
(AM Fat Blocker)

¾ cup vinegar
½ cup water
1 16-oz. can lima beans
1 16 oz. can wax beans
1 15 oz. can kidney beans
1 15 oz. can garbanzo beans
1 16 oz. can green beans
2 tablespoons cornstarch
1 tablespoon sugar

1. Combine cornstarch, sugar, vinegar, and water in skillet and whisk. Cook and stir to boiling
2. Add the beans to skillet, just stirring to mix. Simmer for 20 minutes.

Makes 8 servings.

Edita's Tip
Don't forget to take a couple "Beano" tablets to make sure you don't get any tummy discomfort from gassy foods. You can find beano in your favorite grocery store—usually right next to the beans. Handy, right?

Savory Roasted Vegetables & Pasta
(AM Fat Blocker)

4 carrots, thinly sliced
2 red bell peppers, seeded and cut into strips
2 zucchini, cut into small chunks
2 yellow squash, cut into small chunks
1 teaspoon minced garlic
½ cup non-fat creamer
3 tablespoons Dijon mustard
2 cups penne pasta, cooked
cooking spray

Preheat oven to 425°F

1. Toss vegetables and garlic in roasting pan sprayed with non-fat cooking spray. Bake uncovered, 20 minutes or until tender, stir occasionally.
2. Spoon ½ vegetables in blender. Add creamer and mustard with 2 tbsp. water. Process until smooth.
3. Toss pasta with vegetable puree in large serving bowl. Spoon remaining vegetables on top.

Makes 4 servings.

Edita's Tip
If you want to get skinny faster, turn this into a fat-burner lunch by simply losing the pasta!

Mama Mia Minestrone
(AM Fat Blocker)

4 carrots, peeled, chopped
2 onions, peeled, chopped
3 tomatoes, peeled, chopped
2 celery stalks, chopped
½ small head cabbage, shredded
5 cups water
½ cup elbow macaroni
½ teaspoon black pepper
1 teaspoon chopped parsley

1. Add vegetables to a large cooking add water and pepper; simmer about 30 minutes
2. Add macaroni; cook 20 minutes or until tender. Sprinkle with parsley.

Makes 4 servings.

Edita's Tip
Enjoy this with homemade Italian bread sticks, or drop a few croutons into your bowl and pour the soup over them.

Tomato Surprise Soup
(AM Fat Blocker)

4 potatoes, peeled
2 cups vegetable bouillon
3 medium carrots, cut into large slivers
1 cup snap beans, cut in ½
½ cup celery, chopped
2 tomatoes, halved

1. Put potatoes in saucepan with 1 cup bouillon; bring to boil. Cook, uncovered, 5 minutes; cover. Simmer 15 minutes or until tender.
2. In another saucepan, cook carrots and beans in remaining bouillon, uncovered, 5 minutes; cover. Cook 5 minutes. Add celery; cook 5 minute.
3. Put tomato halves under broiler until desired tenderness. Arrange in bowls with drained vegetables.

Makes 4 servings.

Edita's Tip
Tomatoes are wonderful, proven protection against prostate cancer, so enjoy them often.

Baked Potato With Black Bean Chili
(AM Fat Blocker)

1 large potato
½ cup black bean meatless chili or black bean soup
2 tablespoons salsa
2 tablespoons chopped scallions
1 tablespoon cilantro

1. Scrub potato and cook in microwave until tender.
2. Remove and heat black bean chili or soup separately until warm.
3. Cut slit in potato and top with black bean chili or soup, salsa, scallions, and cilantro.

Makes 1 serving.

Edita's Tip
Use salsa as often as you can. It's better than ketchup and the spicy heat of salsa will crank up your own fat burning thermostat and help you get skinny faster.

Confetti Rice Salad
(AM Fat Blocker)

1 ½ cups cooked brown or white rice, chilled
1 tomato, diced
¼ green pepper, diced
¼ red pepper, diced
1 onion, minced
½ teaspoon chopped parsley
4 tablespoons reduced fat Italian dressing
¼ teaspoon curry
¼ cup raisins

1. Place rice in a large mixing bowl. Add vegetables, dressing, curry and raisins. Toss lightly.

Makes 4 servings.

Edita's Tip
The more color in your meals, the more antioxidants. This is especially important as you lose fat and get skinny.

Marinated Raw Vegetable Salad
(AM Fat Blocker)

8 cups assorted fresh veggies: zucchini and carrot sticks, mushroom and cucumber slices, cherry tomatoes, broccoli and cauliflower florets, tiny cooked potatoes.
½ cup lemon juice
½ teaspoon sugar
1 teaspoon oregano
¼ teaspoon pepper
½ teaspoon dill weed
¼ teaspoon salt

1. Place vegetables in a shallow casserole dish.
2. Combine remaining ingredients in cup. Mix up. Pour over veggies.
3. Refrigerate for several hours. Stir occasionally. Serve.

Makes 8 servings.

Edita's Tip
You can make this wonderful salad with whatever veggies you have on hand. It's a great way to use leftover veggies.

Split Pea Soup
(AM Fat Blocker)

2 cans split pea soup
4 cups water
1 cup chopped onion
2 carrots, chopped
2 stalks celery, chopped
2 garlic cloves, minced
2 teaspoons brown mustard
salt & pepper to taste

1. Combine all ingredients in a large pot. Bring to a boil. Reduce heat and simmer 10 minutes.

Makes 8 servings.

Edita's Tip
A quick version of this is just open a can of split pea soup, add a can of water and the veggies. Simmer until the veggies are tender and enjoy.

Middle Eastern Falafel
(AM Fat Blocker)

1 potato, cooked, peeled and diced
1 can (15-ounces) garbanzo beans, drained
1 onion, peeled and chopped fine
½ cup fresh parsley, chopped fine
1 teaspoon garlic, minced
2 tablespoons tahini
2 tablespoons soy sauce
½ teaspoon turmeric
½ teaspoon coriander
1 teaspoon cumin
¼ teaspoon cayenne

Preheat oven to 350°F
1. Mash the potato and beans together in a mixing bowl.
2. Add the remaining ingredients and mix well.
3. Form the mixture into small patties (about the size of a flattened golf ball) and arrange in a single layer on the cookie sheet. Bake for 15 minutes per side. Serve.

Makes 24 falafel patties.   One serving is 2 patties.

Edita's Tip
I used to love this treat purchased on 5ᵗʰ Avenue in Manhattan from a street vendor with a yellow wagon and a striped umbrella. I'd take my lunch to the steps of the Metropolitan Museum and watch the world stroll by. Try enjoying your lunch outside in a park.

Russian Red Borscht With Potatoes
(AM Fat Blocker)

2 beets, peeled and sliced
1 onion, peeled and chopped
2 carrots, peeled and sliced thin
3 celery stalks, sliced thin
2 cups cabbage, shredded thin
2 cans (15-ounces each) vegetable broth
1 can (15-ounces) crushed tomatoes
4 cups water
1 teaspoon dill weed
½ teaspoon caraway seeds
¼ teaspoon pepper
1 cup sauerkraut
4 potatoes, cooked and quartered

1. Put all the ingredients in the pot, except the sauerkraut, and simmer, covered, on medium heat for 30 minutes.
2. Add the sauerkraut and potatoes. Heat another minute or two. Serve.

Makes 8 servings.

Edita's Tip
This is a recipe I remember from my childhood. My mother would ladle big bowls full of this wonderful rich, red soup and give us thick slices of black bread or pumpernickel to enjoy with it.

Mulligatawny Soup
(AM Fat Blocker)

¼ cup onion, chopped
½ teaspoon curry powder
1 teaspoon reduced fat margarine
1 potato, cooked, peeled and diced
½ cup rice, cooked
1 apple, peeled, cored, and chopped
¼ cup celery, chopped
1 green pepper, seeded and chopped
3 tablespoons flour
4 cups chicken broth
1 can (16 ounces) seasoned tomatoes
2 teaspoons lemon juice
¼ cup parsley, chopped
2 whole cloves

1. Heat the oil in the stock pot and cook the onion and curry powder until the onion is tender about 3 to 5 minutes.
2. Stir in the potato, rice, apple, celery, and green pepper. Cook, stirring occasionally about 5 minutes, until the vegetables are tender but still crisp.
3. Sprinkle the flour over the vegetables and stir to mix well. Add the remaining ingredients and bring to a boil, then reduce the heat and simmer for 15 minutes. Serve hot.

Makes 8 servings.

Delta Corn Salad
(AM Fat Blocker)

2 cups rice, cooked
1 cup corn kernels, cooked
½ cup celery, chopped fine
¼ cup green onion, chopped fine
¼ cup reduced fat Italian dressing
2 tablespoons tomato juice
¼ teaspoon hot pepper sauce

1. Place all the ingredients in a large salad bowl. Toss to coat. Serve.

Makes 4 servings.

Couscous With Herbs
(AM Fat Blocker)

1 box (5.5 ounces) herbed chicken couscous mix
1 red pepper, seeded and diced fine
1 yellow squash, seeded and diced fine
1 cup broccoli, chopped fine
cooking spray

1. Cook the couscous according to package directions.
2. In a nonstick skillet sprayed with cooking spray, sauté the vegetables until crisp tender.
3. In a large bowl, combine the hot vegetables and the couscous. Serve.

Makes 4 servings.   Serving size: 1 cup

Cairo Bulgur Salad
(AM Fat Blocker)

½ cup bulgur
½ cup hot water
¼ cup lemon juice
1 cup peas, frozen and thawed
¼ cup mint, chopped fine
1 tablespoons olive oil
salt and pepper to taste

1. Place the bulgur, lemon juice and hot water in a bowl, stir and let sit for 20 minutes or until the liquid is all absorbed. Fluff with a fork.
2. Add the remaining ingredients and mix together. Serve.

Makes 4 servings.

Edita's Tip
The first time I tried this wonderful nutty, flavorful grain I fell in love with it. I hope you will too! Try filling a hollowed out tomato with this salad, or scoop out a baked potato and fill the baked potato shell with bulgar for an exciting change!

Grilled Romaine Hearts
(AM Fat Blocker)

2 tomatoes, seeded and chopped fine
2 celery stalks, chopped fine
¼ cup parsley, chopped fine
1 Kirby cucumber, peeled, seeded and chopped fine
½ cup green onion, chopped fine
½ cup croutons, garlic flavored
¼ cup reduced fat Italian dressing
½ teaspoon salt
¼ teaspoon pepper
1 tablespoon brown sugar
1 tablespoon balsamic vinegar
2 tablespoons olive oil
4 romaine lettuce hearts

1. In the salad shaker combing the Italian dressing, brown sugar, balsamic vinegar, salt and pepper.
2. Using a pastry brush, brush olive oil over the Romaine hearts until well coated. Sprinkle a little salt and pepper on each heart. Grill on high heat, about 5 to 10 minutes until the leaves are slightly charred but not soft or cooked through, turning often.
3. In a smaller mixing bowl combine the tomatoes, celery, parsley, cucumber, croutons, and green onion and mix well.
4. Arrange the grilled hearts on the platter. Pile the remaining vegetables around the romaine and serve.

Makes 4 servings.

Delicious Fruit Salad
(AM Fat Blocker)

1 can (11 ounces) mandarin orange sections, drained
1 can (8 ounces) pineapple chunks, drained
1 orange, peeled, seeded and cut into chunks
1 pear, cored, seeded and cut into chunks
4 cups Bibb lettuce, torn into bite-size pieces
1 cup nonfat whipped topping

1. Combine the fruit in the salad bowl and mix well.
2. Line the large plate with the lettuce and spoon the salad onto the lettuce. Top with the whipped topping.

Makes 4 servings.

Pepper Salad

(AM Fat Blocker)

12 ounces spinach, leaves
1 red bell pepper, seeded, and sliced into short strips
1 green bell pepper, seeded, and sliced into short strips
1 small onion, sliced thin
1 potato, peeled, cooked and diced
½ cup croutons
1/3 cup reduced fat Italian dressing
3 tablespoons red wine vinegar
½ teaspoon red chili powder
½ teaspoon garlic powder

1. Place the spinach, peppers, onion, potato, and croutons, in a salad bowl.

2. In a small bowl, blend the dressing, vinegar, chili powder and, garlic powder.

3. Pour the dressing over the salad.

Makes 4 servings.

Edita's Tip
Spinach is wonderful source of calcium, but remember to always make sure you sprinkle your spinach with a little lemon juice or vinegar to release the bone-building calcium.

Mexican Salad
(AM Fat Blocker)

1 16-ounce can black beans, drained
2 cups onion, chopped fine
1 teaspoon garlic powder
1 20-ounce can seasoned tomatoes, chopped and drained
1 green pepper, seeded and chopped
1 yellow pepper, seeded and chopped
¼ cup raisins
2 tablespoons chili powder
1 tablespoon cumin
1/8 teaspoon crushed red peppers
salt and pepper to taste

1. In a microwave-safe bowl, combine the beans, the onion, the garlic powder, and the tomatoes. Cover and cook on medium power for 5-7 minutes or until onions are tender.
2. Add the, raisins, peppers, and spices. Cook for 5 more minutes
3. Serve on a bed of greens garnished with sliced lettuce, and salsa. Serve with hot tortilla chips.

Makes 4 servings.

Edita's Tip
Serve this with a basket of corn muffins or corn chips and you've got a great fat-blocker lunch that will help you lose up to a pound a day!

Indian Curry Rice Salad
(AM Fat Blocker)

1 cup rice, cooked
½ cup celery, chopped
¼ cup red pepper, seeded and chopped
¼ cup green pepper, seeded and chopped
4 cherry tomatoes, halved
¼ cup reduced fat Italian salad dressing
1 teaspoon curry powder
1 teaspoon lemon juice

1. Combine the rice, celery, peppers and tomatoes.
2. Mix together the salad dressing, curry and lemon juice and pour over the salad. Toss to combine.

Makes 2 servings.

Edita's Tip
Research shows that curry can speed up your fat melting metabolic power. So enjoy this lunch and make it as hot and spicy as you can stand.

Tuscan Salad
(AM Fat Blocker)

4 cups day-old Italian or French bread, cut into cubes
2 tomatoes, cut into bite-size chunks
1 green pepper, seeded and cut into chunks
½ cup green onion, chopped
1 teaspoon garlic, minced
1/3 cup fresh basil leaves, chopped
2 tablespoons fresh parsley, chopped
¼ cup olive oil
2 tablespoons balsamic vinegar
½ teaspoon salt
½ teaspoon pepper

1. Place all ingredients in a large salad bowl.
2. Toss to coat well. Cover. Let flavors blend for 1 hour before serving.

Makes 4 servings.

Edita's Tip
A bowl of green and black olives makes a wonderful accompaniment to this salad, so Italian you can almost see the Mediterranean with every bite.

Harvest Salad
(AM Fat Blocker)

4 potatoes, cooked, peeled, and cubed
1 ½ cup apples, cored and chopped
1cup celery, diced
¼ cup raisins
1/3 cup reduced fat Italian dressing

1. In a large mixing bowl stir together the apples, celery and raisins.
2. Pour the dressing over the ingredients. Toss lightly until coated.

Makes 4 servings.

Edita's Tip
Garnish with endive leaves, sliced cucumbers and tomato wedges and toss in a few wholewheat crackers.

Mykenos Salad
(AM Fat Blocker)

1 ½ cups instant rice, uncooked
1 large tomato, seeded and diced
1 cup chopped green pepper, seeded and diced
½ cup mushrooms, chopped fine
½ cup chopped green olives
¼ cup green onion, chopped fine
¼ cup celery, chopped fine
½ cup reduced fat Italian dressing
salt and pepper to taste
fresh basil leaves for garnish

1. Prepare rice according to package directions. Set aside to cool.
2. When cool toss the rice with all the remaining ingredients until well coated and combined. Serve on lettuce leaves and garnish with fresh basil leaves. Serve with garlic bread.

Makes 4 servings.

Edita's Tip
If you don't have time to cook up rice for this salad, toss in a handful or two of sesame crackers or heap big spoonfuls of it onto toasted English muffins.

Potato & Corn Chowder
(AM Fat Blocker)

3 cups water
1 small onion, diced
3 medium potatoes, unpeeled and diced
2 stalk celery, chopped
2 carrots, sliced fine
1 can corn kernels, drained
1 teaspoon dill weed
salt and pepper to taste
2 cans evaporated skimmed milk
2 tablespoons flour

1. Combine the water, onions, potatoes, celery carrots, corn, and spices in a large soup pot.
2. Cover and simmer for 15 minutes.
3. Add one of the cans of evaporated milk.
4. In a small bowl, blend the flour and the remaining can of evaporated milk.
5. Whisk until smooth. Slowly stir the flour and milk mixture into the chowder.
6. Simmer another 10 minutes.

Makes 8 servings.

Edita's Tip
Pour this soup into individual oven proof bowls. Float a slice of toasted bread sprinkled with a little Parmesan cheese on top—just a little.

Caribbean Rice & Peas
(AM Fat Blocker)

2 teaspoons olive oil
1 onion, peeled and chopped
½ teaspoon garlic powder
1 cup salsa
1 cup peas, frozen
1 small carrot, peeled and chopped
1 cup beans, cooked or canned and drained
2 cups cooked rice, white or brown
1 tablespoon chili powder

1. Heat the oil in a nonstick skillet.
2. Cook the garlic, onion, peas and carrots over low heat until the carrot is soft and the peas are no longer frozen.
3. Add the salsa and cook 5 minutes more.
4. Add the beans, rice and chili powder. Cook 5 minutes. Serve hot.

Makes 6 servings.

Edita's Tip
I like this dish sprinkled with a little shredded coconut. It makes me feel like I'm sitting on a warm and sandy beach listening to a Calypso band.

Potato & Leek Soup
(AM Fat Blocker)

1 can cream of potato soup
1 bunch leeks, washed and sliced thin
1 can beef broth
¼ cup parsley, chopped
¼ teaspoon dried thyme
¼ teaspoon pepper

1. In a saucepan over medium-high heat, simmer the leeks in the beef broth for 5 to 7 minutes until just softened.
2. Add the can of potato soup. Mix well. Simmer until heated through.
3. Stir in the thyme and parsley. Serve.

Makes 4 servings.

Edita's Tip
On a cold day serve this soup hot. On a hot summer day,
chill the soup and serve it cold.
Delicious and quick, either way.

Pasta & Rice Skillet Casserole
(AM Fat Blocker)

1 tablespoon margarine
½ cup onion, chopped
½ cup red or green pepper, seeded and chopped
½ cup celery, chopped
1 carrot, peeled and chopped
1 cup rice, brown or white
2 ounces spaghetti, broken
2 cups chicken broth
1 cup water
½ teaspoon dried thyme
salt and pepper to taste
¼ cup fresh parsley, chopped

1. In a large skillet over medium-high heat, melt the margarine. Add the onion, peppers, celery and carrot. Cook, stirring occasionally, until the vegetables are soft, about 3 minutes.
2. Add the rice and spaghetti and cook, stirring, until lightly browned. Add the remaining ingredients, except the parsley. Bring to a boil.
3. Reduce heat. Cover and simmer 30 to 40 minutes or until the rice and spaghetti are cooked. Stir in the parsley. Serve hot.

Makes 6 servings.

Edita's Tip
I love this casserole with a bowl of homemade relish, or a couple of crunchy dill pickles.

Hotel Waldorf Lunch Salad
(AM Fat Blocker)

2 apples, peeled, cored and chopped
2 pears, cored and chopped
2 oranges, peeled, seeded and chopped
½ cup celery, chopped
½ cup raisins
½ cup walnuts, chopped
¼ cup low fat mayonnaise
1 teaspoon lemon juice

1. In a medium bowl combine all the ingredients. Toss.
2. Cover and chill for 1 hour before serving.

Makes 6 servings.

Edita's Tip
Add a few mini marshmallows to this salad and even the kids will love it.

Potato & Bean Salad
(AM Fat Blocker)

8 red potatoes, scrubbed and cooked
¾ cup white kidney beans, canned and drained
½ cup red pepper, seeded and chopped
½ cup green pepper, seeded and chopped
½ cup celery, chopped
½ cup onion, chopped
¼ cup olive oil
2 tablespoons balsamic vinegar
¾ teaspoon dill weed
salt and pepper to taste

1. Cut the potatoes into quarters.
2. In a large mixing bowl combine all the ingredients. Toss to coat well.
3. Cover and chill 1 hour.

Makes 6 servings.

Edita's Tip
I like to wrap big spoonfuls of this salad in romaine lettuce leaves for a wonderful skinny wrap.

Quick Potato Pancakes
(AM Fat Blocker)

1 package hash brown potato mix
4 cups hot water
1 teaspoon salt
¼ teaspoon pepper
1 onion, grated
2 eggs, beaten
3 tablespoons vegetable oil

1. In a large bowl cover the potatoes with the hot water. Add the salt. Let stand uncovered 15 minutes. Drain.
2. Add the onion, eggs and pepper to the potatoes. Mix thoroughly.
3. In a large skillet, heat the oil one tablespoon at a time.
4. Using a large ladle or serving spoon, spoon about a ¼ cup of the potato mixture into the skillet and press into the shape of a flat patty.
5. Cook for 2 minutes or until brown and crispy.
6. Turn over and cook the other side until brown and crispy.
7. Place on a paper towel to absorb any oil. Repeat the process until all the batter is used up. Serve warm.

Makes 4 servings.

Edita's Tip
Add a bowl of fresh applesauce and nonfat yogurt or sour cream and you've got a true old-world taste treat.

Basil Bruschetta With Tomatoes
(AM Fat Blocker)

12 slices Italian bread cut into ½ inch thick slices
4 Italian tomatoes, seeded and chopped
1/3 cup fresh basil, chopped
1 teaspoon garlic, minced
¼ cup olive oil
2 tablespoons balsamic vinegar
salt and pepper to taste

Preheat oven to 400°F.
1. Toast the bread slices in a single layer on a nonstick cookie sheet in the oven for 3 to 5 minutes per side, until each side is a light, golden brown.
2. In a large mixing bowl combine the remaining ingredients. Toss.
3. Spoon the tomato mixture onto the toasted bread, dividing it evenly.

Makes 4 servings.

Edita's Tip
This is often served as an appetizer—a tempting taste of Italy—just before an exciting pasta dish. But it makes one of the best fat blocking lunches, ever!

Sweet Potato Salad
(AM Fat Blocker)

3 sweet potatoes
1 green pepper, seeded and chopped
2 stalks celery, seeded and chopped
3 spring onions, chopped
¼ cup walnuts or pecans, chopped
1 teaspoon fresh ginger, grated
4 ounces tofu
2 tablespoons olive oil
2 tablespoons cider vinegar
1 tablespoon lemon juice
1 tablespoon soy sauce

1. Boil the sweet potatoes whole in their skins.
2. When the potatoes are cooked, cube them and then gently mix in the pepper, celery, onions, nuts, and ginger.
3. In a small bowl, blend together the tofu, olive oil, vinegar, lemon juice and soy sauce. Pour over the potatoes. Toss.

Makes 6 servings.

Edita's Tip
Sweet potatoes are one of the best natural sources of beta carotene a powerful cancer fighting antioxidant. So go ahead. Enjoy an extra spoonful.

Spanish Rice
(AM Fat Blocker)

2 tablespoons olive oil
1 onion, peeled and chopped
1 red bell pepper, seeded and diced
2 teaspoons garlic, minced
1 teaspoon fresh ginger, peeled and grated
1 package (10 ounces) spinach, thawed and chopped
¼ pound mushrooms, sliced
1 cup rice, uncooked
1 teaspoon soy sauce
2 cups chicken broth

1. Heat the oil in a nonstick skillet on medium-high heat and cook the onion, pepper, garlic, and ginger until the onion and pepper are soft, about 5 minutes.
2. Add the spinach and cook, stirring often for 2 minutes, then add the mushrooms, cooking for another 2 minutes.
3. Add the rice, soy sauce and chicken broth and bring the mixture to a boil. Cover. Reduce heat and simmer for 20 minutes until the liquid is absorbed. Fluff with a fork and serve.

Makes 4 servings.

Edita's Tip
Ginger is nature's own tummy soother designed to reduce bloating, gas and heartburn. Add ginger to some of your own favorite recipes and see how great you'll feel.

Chicken Chow Mein
(PM Fat Burner)

2 cups chicken, cooked and sliced
1 green sweet pepper, sliced
1 red sweet pepper, sliced
½ cup mushrooms, sliced
1 small onion
2 stalks celery, sliced
1 tablespoon flour
2 cups chicken broth
2 tablespoons low sodium soy sauce
¼ cup toasted almonds

1. Spray skillet with non-stick cooking spray and sauté vegetable, stirring constantly for about 5 minutes.
2. Pour in broth, flour, and soy sauce and simmer uncovered for about 10 minutes.
3. Add chicken, stir, cover and simmer on low heat for an additional 10 minutes.
4. Top with almonds and serve.

Makes 4 servings.

Edita's Tip
Just remember, you can enjoy all your favorite foods, just keep your fat blocker carbs for the AM hours, and your fat burner proteins for PM and that way you'll be able to lose up to a pound or more in every 24 hour period.

Balsamic Chicken Cucumber Salad
(PM Fat Burner)

2 cups pre-cooked chicken, cubed
1 medium cucumber, sliced
8 cups salad greens
1 small red onion, sliced
6 tbsp. balsamic vinegar
½ tsp. sugar
3 tbsp. olive oil

Combine vegetables and chicken in salad bowl and toss.
Mix vinegar, sugar, and oil in jar; shake well. Pour dressing
on salad and toss lightly. Makes 8 servings.

Turkish Salad
(PM Fat Burner)

2 cups of diced ham
2 large cucumbers, diced
Dressing:
1 cup plain yogurt
1 teaspoon yellow mustard
2 mint leaves, ground
2 tablespoons chopped chives
1/8 teaspoon nutmeg

Combine ham and cucumbers. Prepare dressing separately
by combining all ingredients. Fold ham and cucumbers into
prepared dressing. Makes 4 servings.

Spinach & Bacon & Feta Cheese Salad
(PM Fat Burner)

10 cups torn spinach
6 slices bacon, cooked crisp and crumbled
½ cup slice red onion
1 cup crumble Feta cheese
¼ cup slivered almonds
½ cup fat free Italian dressing

Toss spinach, oranges, onion, and cheese in large bowl.
Add dressing and toss lightly

Makes 10 servings.

Edita's Tip
If you like, feel free to substitute diced smoked ham for the
bacon, and cheddar or mozzarella for the feta cheese.

Baked Ham Steak
(PM Fat Burner)

1 lb. ready to serve ham steak
1 can (8 oz.) crushed unsweetened pineapple, drained
1 cup diced red or green bell peppers
3 tbsp. honey mustard
1/16 tsp. ground cloves
1 tsp. brown sugar

Preheat oven to 425°F
1. Place ham in baking dish. Combine remaining ingredients in small bowl. Top ham with mixture. Bake, uncovered, 20 minutes.

Makes 4 servings.

Edita's Tip
This dish works very well with hot, cooked apple slices. Just peel, core and slice a couple of apples. Cook them in a tablespoon of water in the microwave and substitute for the pineapple. Don't forget to dust the apples with a little cinnamon for extra fat burning power.

Oil & Vinegar Chicken Salad
(PM Fat Burner)

1 tablespoon olive oil
¼ cup honey mustard
2 tablespoons balsamic vinegar
1 teaspoon minced onion
8 cups mixed salad greens, washed and torn
2 cups chicken, cooked and cubed
½ cup feta cheese, crumbled

1. Whisk together oil, mustard, vinegar, onion, 2 tablespoons vinegar in bowl.
2. Arrange salad greens, chicken, cheese in bowls. Pour on mixture.

Makes 4 servings.

Edita's Tip
This salad makes a wonderful light dinner. Serve it hot with sliced green beans topped with slivered almonds or chopped peanuts.

Max's Salad
(PM Fat Burner)

8 cups mixed salad greens
1 medium onion, sliced
1 clove garlic, chopped
½ teaspoon paprika
¼ cup lemon juice
½ cup Roquefort cheese, crumbled

1. Wash lettuce well and drain. Shake dry; tear into bite-size pieces. Combine with onion in large salad bowl.
2. Combine garlic, paprika, lemon juice in small bowl; mix with fork. Pour over salad; toss. Sprinkle with cheese.

Makes 4 servings.

Edita's Tip
Garlic is powerful medicine. Enjoy it often for its healthy and fat melting benefits.

Marinated Beef Salad
(PM Fat Burner)

3 cups cubed cooked lean beef
½ cup onion, chopped
2 tablespoons. chopped parsley
1 sweet red pepper, seeded, chopped
1 medium tomato, chopped
1 large tomato, cut into wedges
1 head lettuce

Dressing:

½ cup red wine vinegar
¼ teaspoon black pepper
½ teaspoon oregano
½ teaspoon yellow mustard

1. Combine beef, onion, parsley, pepper, tomato in medium bowl; toss well. Combine dressing ingredients together in medium bowl; pour over salad; toss well. Refrigerate at least 3 hours.
2. Arrange lettuce and large tomato wedges in large bowl; fill with salad.

Makes 4 servings.

Edita's Tip
Did you know that beef has gotten skinnier? So you can enjoy it often as a major fat burning food to get you skinny and keep you skinny!

Dutch Egg Salad
(PM Fat Burner)

4 hard-boiled eggs, sliced
2 anchovy fillets, diced
1 medium tomato
1 small cucumber, diced
½ cup plain yogurt
1 ½ teaspoons yellow mustard
1 teaspoons lemon juice

1. Combine eggs, anchovies, tomato, cucumber in large bowl and set aside.
2. Combine remaining ingredients in a small bowl. Mix well; top ingredients in large bowl.

Makes 4 servings.

Edita's Tip
If you have concerns about cholesterol, discard three of the hard-boiled egg yolks and make the salad with four egg whites and just one egg yolk.

Olive Grove Cheese Salad
(PM Fat Burner)

1 cup feta cheese, crumbles
½ teaspoon ground black pepper
2 tablespoons olive oil
2 tablespoons white vinegar
3 stalks celery, thinly sliced
10 pecans

1. Arrange cheese in salad bowl. Sprinkle generously with pepper. Drizzle 1 tbsp. each oil and vinegar over cheese.
2. Arrange celery on cheese. Sprinkle with nuts. Drizzle rest of oil and vinegar.
3. Cover: refrigerate at least 1 hour. Mix well.

Makes 4 servings.

Edita's Tip
I LOVE this salad. It's different. Has a rich exciting new taste. Scoop it into big leaves of romaine lettuce or endive.

Classic Chef's Salad
(PM Fat Burner)

½ head Boston lettuce
1 large tomato, cut into eighths
½ cucumber, thinly sliced
1 small onion, sliced thin
½ green pepper, cut into thin strips
½ cup cooked chicken, cut into strips
½ cup cooked ham, cut into strips
¼ cup low-fat mozzarella cheese
1 egg, cooked and crumbled

1. Wash lettuce; tear into bite-size pieces. Arrange on platter with tomato, cucumber, onion, and green pepper. Arrange meats, cheese, and egg on top. Drizzle with your favorite reduced fat dressing.

Makes 4 servings.

Edita's Tip
This classic dish is wonderful with a splash of balsamic vinegar or a splash of lime juice.

Shrimp and Broccoli Salad
(PM Fat Burner)

1 cup chopped broccoli
1 cup sliced mushrooms
½ cup sliced celery
½ cup green onions
½ cup fat-free Italian dressing
1 cup frozen popcorn shrimp, cooked

1. Combine all ingredients except shrimp. Chill for an hour.
2. Just before serving, stir in shrimp.

Makes 4 servings.

Edita's Tip
Stand up straight. It's a good way to look five pounds thinner. Now smile!

Asparagus Salad With Egg & Bacon
(PM Fat Burner)

½ cup reduced fat mayonnaise
2 tablespoons nonfat French dressing
2 tablespoons pickle relish
2 tablespoons balsamic vinegar
¼ cup fresh parsley, chopped fine
1 tablespoon pimento, chopped
1 package asparagus spears, frozen
2 hard-boiled eggs, sliced
2 slices bacon, crisply cooked and crumbled
4 large Romaine lettuce leaves

1. In a small bowl mix together the mayonnaise, French dressing, pickle relish, vinegar, parsley, and pimento. Cover and chill.
2. Cook asparagus according to package directions. Chill.
3. Place a leaf of Romaine on each plate. Divide the asparagus evenly and top with egg slices. Spoon the dressing over each serving and sprinkle with bacon. Serve.

Makes 4 servings.

Edita's Tip
If asparagus is not in season, try this salad with chilled steamed broccoli or green beans.

Russian Red Borscht With Smoked Ham
(PM Fat Burner)

2 beets, peeled and sliced
1 onion, peeled and chopped
2 carrots, peeled and sliced thin
3 celery stalks, sliced thin
2 cups cabbage, shredded thin
2 cans (15-ounces each) vegetable broth
1 can (15-ounces) crushed tomatoes
4 cups water
1 teaspoon dill weed
½ teaspoon caraway seeds
¼ teaspoon pepper
1 cup sauerkraut
1 cup smoked ham, chopped

3. Put all the ingredients in the pot, except the sauerkraut, and simmer, covered, on medium heat for 30 minutes.
4. Add the sauerkraut and ham. Heat another minute or two. Serve.

Makes 8 servings.

Edita's Tip
This is a perfect example of just how easy it is to turn a fat blocking meal into a fat burning one by simply switching out carbs and adding in protein. In this case, the potatoes are out—and smoked ham is in!

Mulligatawny Soup Redux
(PM Fat Burner)

¼ cup onion, chopped
½ teaspoon curry powder
1 teaspoon reduced fat margarine
2 cups chicken, cooked and diced
1 apple, peeled, cored, and chopped
¼ cup celery, chopped
1 green pepper, seeded and chopped
3 tablespoons flour
4 cups chicken broth
1 can (16 ounces) seasoned tomatoes
2 teaspoons lemon juice
¼ cup parsley, chopped
2 whole cloves

4. Heat the oil in the stock pot and cook the onion and curry powder until the onion is tender about 3 to 5 minutes.
5. Stir in the chicken, apple, celery, and green pepper. Cook, stirring occasionally about 5 minutes, until the vegetables are tender but still crisp.
6. Sprinkle the flour over the chicken and vegetables and stir to mix well. Add the remaining ingredients and bring to a boil, then reduce the heat and simmer for 15 minutes. Serve hot.

Makes 8 servings.

Tomato Salad Napoli
(PM Fat Burner)

4 tomatoes, sliced
4 ounces fresh mozzarella, sliced
½ cup fresh basil, chopped
¼ cup reduced fat Italian dressing
salt and pepper to taste

1. Arrange the tomato and cheese slices in alternating order on the platter.
2. Sprinkle with salt, pepper and basil. Drizzle with the salad dressing. Serve.

Makes 4 servings.

Edita's Tip
If you want a little extra zip, try drizzling the salad with a little balsamic vinegar.

Village Salad
(PM Fat Burner)

4 cups cabbage, chopped
½ cup feta cheese, crumbled
1 tablespoon dill
1 tablespoon olive oil
2 tablespoons lemon juice
1 tablespoon Parmesan cheese, grated
¼ teaspoon dry mustard
¼ teaspoon oregano
salt and pepper to taste

1. Place the cabbage, feta and dill in a salad bowl.
2. Mix together, in a salad dressing shaker the remaining ingredients and pour over the cabbage, tossing to coat well. Serve.

Makes 4 servings.

Edita's Tip
I love this salad heated up. Just toss all the ingredients into a big pot. Add a little tomato juice and heat through. Just before serving toss in a little mozzarella cheese instead of the feta and add a little garlic and dill. Makes a great surprising hot salad for a chilly day.

Outrageous Veggie Salad
(PM Fat Burner)

1 cup asparagus, cooked and cut into bite-size chunks
1 cup green beans, cooked and cut into bite-size chunks
2 tomatoes, seeded and chopped into chunks
½ cup leeks, washed and sliced into chunks
½ cup cabbage, steamed and cut into chunks
1 red pepper, seeded and diced
1 head Romaine lettuce, torn into bite-size bits
¼ cup calorie reduced Italian dressing
2 tablespoons Dijon-style prepared mustard

1. Toss all the ingredients together with the salad dressing. Mix well.

Makes 4 servings.

Edita's Tip
New studies show that the addition of mustard can help you burn calories faster, and get skinny sooner.

Mexican Salad with Beef

(PM Fat Burner)

2 cups onion, chopped fine
1 teaspoon garlic powder
1 20-ounce can seasoned tomatoes, chopped and
drained
1 pound lean ground beef
1 green pepper, seeded and chopped
1 yellow pepper, seeded and chopped
2 tablespoons chili powder
1 tablespoon cumin
1/8 teaspoon crushed red peppers
salt and pepper to taste
cooking spray

1. Sautee the onion, garlic powder, and the tomatoes until the onions are tender about 5 minutes
2. Remove. In the same brown the beef. Cook for 5 more minutes or until the beef is well cooked through and through. Drain the mixture well.
3. Add the two mixtures together and combine. Serve on a bed of greens garnished with shredded low fat cheddar cheese, sliced lettuce, and salsa.

Makes 4 servings.

Edita's Tip
Spoonfuls of this mixture are wonderful wrapped in big lettuce leaves.

Picnic Ham Salad
(PM Fat Burner)

2 cups ham, cooked and cut into chunks
½ cup broccoli florets
2 tomatoes, chopped
¼ cup parsley, chopped fine
8 ounces plain, nonfat yogurt
¼ cup Parmesan cheese, grated
1 teaspoon garlic, minced
1 tablespoon Dijon-style mustard

Put all the ingredients into the salad bowl and toss to combine well. Serve. Makes 2 servings.

Niçoise Salad
(PM Fat Burner)

1 package (10 ounces) frozen whole green beans, thawed
4 cups Bibb lettuce, torn into bite-size pieces
2 tomatoes cut into wedges
2 hard-boiled eggs cut into wedges
½ cup pitted olives
4 individual serving cans tuna, packed in water, drained
½ cup nonfat Italian dressing

Arrange the lettuce on the platter.Heap the tuna in the center and surround with the tomatoes, eggs, olives and beans. Pour the dressing on top. Serve. Makes 4 servings.

Chinese Shrimp Salad
(PM Fat Burner)

1 pound shrimp, cooked and drained
2/3 cups celery, finely chopped
¼ cup green onion, finely chopped
¼ cup green pepper, seeded and finely chopped
¼ cup red pepper, seeded and finely chopped
1 8-ounce can of Chinese water chestnuts, halved
10-ounce package frozen snow peas
½ cup reduced fat mayonnaise
4 teaspoons soy sauce

1. Dice the shrimp.
2. In a large bowl combine the onion, peppers, water chestnuts, and snow peas.
3. In a small bowl combine the mayonnaise and soy sauce.
4. Pour the dressing on top. Toss gently to coat. Serve on lettuce leaves.

Makes 8 servings.

Edita's Tip
Try this salad with cooked scallops, or crab. It's fantastic with any seafood you select.

Beef Pepper Salad
(PM Fat Burner)

2 cups onion, chopped fine
1 teaspoon garlic powder
1 20-ounce can seasoned tomatoes, chopped and drained
1 pound lean ground beef
1 green pepper, seeded and chopped
1 yellow pepper, seeded and chopped
2 tablespoons chili powder
1 tablespoon cumin
1/8 teaspoon crushed red peppers
salt and pepper to taste

1. In a microwave-safe bowl, ½ the onion, ½ the garlic powder, and the tomatoes. Cover and cook on medium power for 5-7 minutes or until onions are tender.
2. In a skillet, brown the beef.
3. Add the remaining onion and garlic powder, peppers, and spices. Cook for 5 more minutes or until the beef is well cooked through and through. Drain the mixture.
4. Add the beef mixture into the tomato mixture. Serve hot.

Makes 8 servings.

Edita's Tip
Serve on a bed of greens garnished with shredded low fat cheddar cheese, sliced lettuce, and salsa.

New England Clam Chowder
(PM Fat Burner)

1 can chunky clam chowder prepared soup
1 ½ cup water
2 6-ounce cans minced clams with juice
1 14-ounce can evaporated skim milk

1. In a medium saucepan, combine the vegetable soup, water, and clams.
2. Bring to a boil over medium-high heat.
3. Reduce heat and simmer partially covered for 5 minutes.
4. Stir in the evaporated milk. Heat through, but do not boil.

Makes 4 servings.

Edita's Tip
Add an extra can of minced clams and you won't even miss the potatoes and the fish crackers.

Wicked Deviled Eggs
(PM Fat Burner)

6 hard boiled eggs, cooled
½ cup low fat cheddar cheese, shredded
2 tablespoons fresh parsley, chopped
3 tablespoons low fat mayonnaise
1 teaspoon Dijon mustard
1/8 teaspoon salt
¼ teaspoon pepper

1. Peel the eggs and slice lengthwise in half.
2. Remove yolk. Place yolks in a bowl and mash them with a fork. Add the remaining ingredients and mix well.
3. Fill the egg white cups with the yolk mixture.

Makes 6 servings.

Edita's Tip
I like this served with a couple of slices of deli turkey or sliced chicken.

French Country Tomato Ham Salad
(PM Fat Burner)

2 cups cooked ham, cubed
2 tomatoes, cut into bite-size chunks
1 green pepper, seeded and cut into chunks
½ cup green onion, chopped
½ cup chopped green olives
1 teaspoon garlic, minced
1/3 cup fresh basil leaves, chopped
2 tablespoons fresh parsley, chopped
¼ cup olive oil
2 tablespoons balsamic vinegar
½ teaspoon salt
½ teaspoon pepper

1. Place all ingredients in a large salad bowl. Toss to coat well.
2. Cover. Let flavors blend for 1 hour before serving.

Makes 6 servings.

Edita's Tip
A little chopped egg and parmesan cheese piled on top adds even more fat burning protein to this lush salad.

Sea Chowder Kebabs
(PM Fat Burner)

1 tablespoon olive oil
½ cup onion, chopped
½ cup green pepper, seeded and chopped
½ cup red pepper, seeded and chopped
½ cup celery, chopped
1 teaspoon garlic, minced
1 can (16-ounces) seasoned tomatoes with liquid
1 cup water
¼ cup fresh parsley, chopped
1 bay leaf
1 teaspoon dried basil
½ teaspoon dried thyme
salt and pepper to taste
1 pound halibut, cut into chunks
6 shrimp, 6 scallops, 6 clams with shells

1. In a medium saucepan over medium-high heat, heat the olive oil. Add the onion, green pepper, red pepper, celery, and garlic. Cook, stirring 1 minute.
2. Add the tomatoes, water, and seasonings. Bring to a boil. Reduce heat and simmer 10 minutes.
3. Add the seafood. Continue cooking, covered, for 10 minutes until the fish is tender and flaky.

Makes 6 servings.

Edita's Tip
Alternate the fish with chunks of tomato on skewers. Pour the soup into soup bowls and serve kebabs on the side!

Madras Lamb Salad
(PM Fat Burner)

4 cups cooked lamb, diced
½ cup walnuts, chopped
¼ cup celery, chopped
¼ cup onion, chopped
3 tablespoons vegetable oil
2 tablespoons vinegar
1 teaspoon garlic, minced
1 teaspoon curry powder
½ teaspoon ground cumin
¼ teaspoon ground cinnamon
salt and pepper to taste

1. In a medium mixing bowl combine all the remaining ingredients. Mix well.
2. Cover and chill for 1 hour before serving.

Makes 4 servings.

Edita's Tip
Try to have lamb more often. It is wonderful, tasty, lean and a nice change from beef and chicken.

Luncheon Deli Scramble
(PM Fat Burner)

4 eggs
2 tablespoons skim milk
salt and pepper to taste
½ cup diced onion
1 cup diced ham
cooking spray

1. In a small bowl whisk together the eggs, skim milk, and salt and pepper.
2. In a small nonstick skillet sprayed with cooking spray, cook the onion until softened, about 5 minutes. Add the ham. Cook until the ham is warmed through.
3. Add the eggs and stir until cooked. Serve hot.

Makes 2 servings.

Edita's Tip
All this simple dish needs is a sliced tomato with onion for a perfect fat burning lunch.

Tomato Stuffed With Crab
(PM Fat Burner)

2 large tomatoes, halved and scooped out and reserved
1 cup crab meat, drained
½ cup black olives, chopped
½ cup celery, chopped fine
1 teaspoon garlic, chopped fine
½ cup parsley, chopped fine
½ teaspoon oregano
½ teaspoon dried basil
salt and pepper to taste
¼ cup reduced fat Italian dressing
1 cup reduced fat mozzarella cheese, shredded

1. Combine the reserved scooped out tomato, crab, olives, celery, garlic, spices and dressing in a large bowl and toss to coat well.
2. Divide equally among the tomato halves.
3. Sprinkle with the cheese. Serve.

Option: to serve hot, combine all the ingredients in a nonstick saucepan and heat through. Stuff the tomatoes with the heated mixture. Sprinkle with the cheese and place under the broiler until the cheese melts. Serve hot.

Makes 4 servings.   Serving size: 1 stuffed tomato half

A Little Soul Food
Trust your hopes not your fears.

Caesar Salad With Grilled Salmon
(PM Fat Burner)

2 salmon fillets, grilled and sliced
1 large bunch Romaine lettuce, torn into bits
2 cups cherry tomatoes, halved
1 tablespoon garlic, minced fine
½ cup reduced fat Caesar dressing
1 tablespoon balsamic vinegar
2 tablespoons Parmesan cheese

1. Place the Romaine lettuce in a large salad bowl.
2. In a small glass or shaker combine the dressing, garlic, and balsamic vinegar. Shake and pour over the salad and toss well to combine.
3. Arrange the salmon on top of the salad. Sprinkle with the tomatoes and the Parmesan cheese.

Makes 4 servings.   Serving size: 2 cups

Edita's Tip
Try this with grilled or blackened chicken, shrimp or even generous chunks of ham. Delicious!

Salad Greens With Goat Cheese
(PM Fat Burner)

4 cups salad greens
4 slices goat cheese, cut from a loaf
½ teaspoon oregano
½ teaspoon basil
½ teaspoon marjoram
½ teaspoon thyme
½ cup reduced fat oil and vinegar dressing

Preheat oven to 375°F.

1. In a small bowl combine ¼ cup of the dressing and the spices. Mix well.
2. In a nonstick baking pan place the slices of goat cheese and drizzle them with the dressing. Bake for 15 minutes until the cheese has softened.
3. Arrange the greens on individual plates and top each with a round of the cheese. Drizzle the remaining dressing over the greens. Serve.

Makes 4 servings.

A Little Soul Food
Nothing is hard if you divide it into small jobs.

Shrimp Cocktail Lunch
(PM Fat Burner)

1 pound jumbo shrimp, cooked
1 cup cocktail sauce

1. Pour the cocktail sauce into a small bowl. Place the bowl in the center of a large platter.
2. Pile the shrimp on the platter. Dip shrimp into the sauce and enjoy.

Makes 4 servings.

Edita's Tip
This is so retro and fun. Don't save this wonderful lunch for a special occasion.

Shrimp Salad With Onions
(PM Fat Burner)

1 head Romaine lettuce, torn into bits
1 pound cooked shrimp, chopped
2 stalks celery, chopped fine
1 bunch green onion, chopped fine
1 tablespoon cilantro, chopped fine
1 tablespoon parsley, chopped fine
½ cup reduced fat vinaigrette dressing

1. In a large bowl combine the lettuce shrimp, celery, green onion, cilantro, parsley and dressing. Toss to coat. Serve. Makes 4 servings.

Herbed Yogurt Cheese
(PM Fat Burner)

4 cups nonfat yogurt, plain
1 teaspoon, chopped fine
1 tablespoon parsley, chopped fine
1 teaspoon thyme
1 teaspoon tarragon
1 teaspoon oregano
salt and pepper

1. Place yogurt in a strainer lined with a coffee filter and balance over a large bowl, making sure the bottom of the strainer doesn't touch the bottom of the bowl. Chill until thick about 24 hours.
2. Discard the liquid and mix in the herbs. Season with salt and pepper to taste. Serve.

Makes 8 servings.

Puppies
(PM Fat Burner)

16 cocktail franks
¼ cup barbecue sauce

1. In a small nonstick skillet heat the franks in the barbecue sauce. Serve with toothpicks.

Makes 4 servings.   Serving size: 4 pieces

Smoked Salmon Bites
(PM Fat Burner)

4 slices of smoked salmon
1 package (4 ounces) cream cheese
2 tablespoons fresh dill, chopped
2 tablespoons onion, peeled and chopped fine
2 tablespoons capers, chopped
4 large lettuce leaves

1. Mix the cream cheese with the dill, onion and capers.
2. Spread the cream cheese on the slices of salmon and place each salmon piece on a leaf of lettuce. Roll up and secure with a toothpick. Serve.

Makes 4 servings.   Serving size: 1 stuffed lettuce leaf

Goat Cheese Boats
(PM Fat Burner)

8 ounces goat cheese, at room temperature
½ cup skim milk
24 fresh basil leaves, endive leaves, or celery chunks
1 tomato, chopped fine

1. Combine the cheese and milk and season with salt and pepper to taste.
2. Spread an equal amount of the cheese onto a leaf of fresh basil, endive or piece of celery. Garnish with the chopped tomato. Serve.

Makes 24 servings.   Serving size: 4 pieces

Spiced Nuts
(PM Fat Burner)

1 cup each raw almonds, cashews, pecan halves, peanuts
1 teaspoon each chili powder, curry powder, cumin
2 teaspoons garlic powder
2 tablespoons olive oil

Preheat oven to 350°F.
Toss all the ingredients together in a plastic bag. Shake until the nuts are well coated. Transfer the nuts to a nonstick cookie sheet and bake 15 to 20 minutes, stirring occasionally. Remove and cool. Serve. Makes 4 cups
Serving size: ½ cup

Stuffed Jalapenos
(PM Fat Burner)

12 shrimp, cooked and chopped fine
3 strips of bacon, cut into 12 pieces
12 jalapenos, seeded with tops cut off
4 ounces cream cheese, softened

Preheat oven to 375°F.
Mix together the shrimp and cream cheese. Stuff each jalapeno with the cream cheese mixture and top each stuffed jalapeno with a piece of bacon. Push a toothpick into the bacon to secure. Bake for 30 minutes. Serve. Makes 12 servings. Serving Size: 3 jalapenos.

Crayon Box Dip
(PM Fat Burner)

1 container (16-ounces) nonfat sour cream
1 envelope Italian salad dressing mix
1 green pepper, seeded and chopped fine
1 red pepper, seeded and chopped fine
1 yellow pepper, seeded and chopped fine

1. Combine all the ingredients in a mixing bowl.
2. Chill until flavors combine about 2 hours. Makes 8 servings.

Chili Cheese Dip
(PM Fat Burner)

1 cup plain, nonfat yogurt
½ cup nonfat cottage cheese
1 teaspoon garlic, minced
2 tablespoons green chilies, chopped
1 teaspoon chili powder
1/8 teaspoon black pepper

1. Combine all the ingredients in a mixing bowl.
2. Chill until flavors combine about 2 hours. Makes 4 servings.

Edita's Tip
Try serving these dips in a hollowed out green, red or yellow pepper! And dunk lots of cut up veggies, endive or lettuce leaves.

Stuffed Celery
(PM Fat Burner)

1 cup cooked chicken or ham, chopped fine
¼ cup nonfat mayonnaise
1 red pepper, seeded and chopped fine
2 tablespoons skim milk
1 tablespoon Dijon-style mustard
¼ teaspoon red pepper flakes
8 stalks of celery

1. In a mixing bowl combine the chicken, mayonnaise, red pepper, milk, mustard, and pepper flakes.
2. Blend well and stuff the chicken mixture into the celery, dividing equally.

Makes 8 servings. One serving is 2 stuffed celery stalks

Edita's Tip
You can also make this snack with tuna or salmon.

Salmon Rolls
(PM Fat Burner)

½ pound smoked salmon, sliced thin
1 package (4 ounces) reduced fat cream cheese

1. Spread thin slices of salmon with a little of the cream cheese and roll up securing with a toothpick.
2. Cut each salmon roll into ½ inch slices.
Makes 4 servings.

Curried Nuts
(PM Fat Burner)

1/3 cup blanched whole almonds
1/3 cup blanched peanuts
1/3 cup walnut or pecan halves
1 teaspoon reduced fat margarine
1 teaspoon curry powder
1/8 teaspoon pepper
1/8 teaspoon salt

Preheat oven to 325°F
1. In a small saucepan over low heat, melt the margarine. Add the curry, pepper and salt and cook, stirring for another minute.
2. Place the nuts in a plastic bag and pour the spice mixture over them, shaking the bag to coat well. Spread in a single layer on a nonstick cookie sheet and bake for 15 to 20 minutes.

Makes 4 servings.

Edita's Tip
Try different combinations of nuts and seasonings to create endless variations on this snack.

Spicy Chicken Tenders
(PM Fat Burner)

16 skinless, boneless chicken tenders
¼ cup lemon juice
¼ cup barbecue sauce
¼ cup of tomato paste

Preheat oven 350° F.

Mix tomato paste, barbecue sauce and lemon juice in bowl with spoon. Add chicken tenders to mixture and stir to coat evenly with sauce. Spread out on baking sheet covered with tinfoil and bake for about 30 min. Makes 4 servings. Serving size: 4 tenders

Edita's Tip
Heat up a little extra barbecue sauce for dipping.

Cheesy Dogs
(PM Fat Burner)

2 hot dogs, split lengthwise but not quite through
2 slices of American cheese, cut into strips

Preheat broiler

1. Stuff the hot dogs with the cheese strips and broil until the cheese melts. Serve hot.

Makes 2 servings.

Seafood & Lime Paté
(PM Fat Burner)

3 eggs, hard boiled, peeled and chopped fine
1 teaspoon reduced fat margarine
1 teaspoon garlic, minced
1 bunch green onions, chopped fine
½ pound scallops
½ pound shrimp, cooked
1 can (6 ounces) crabmeat, drained
1 package (8 ounces) reduced fat cream cheese, softened
2 tablespoons Dijon mustard
2 tablespoons prepared horseradish
3 tablespoons lime juice
salt and pepper to taste

1. In a large nonstick skillet heat the margarine and add the garlic, scallions, and scallops. Sauté until scallops are cooked, about 5 minutes.
2. Add the shrimp and crabmeat and cook another 2 minutes.
3. Transfer the mixture to a food processor and blend until smooth.

Makes 8 servings.

Edita's Tip
I like this served in a chilled bowl and garnished with slices of orange, lemon and lime. Actually it tastes great if you pile a little on an orange slice and enjoy!

Crabmeat & Cucumber Bites
(PM Fat Burner)

1 package (8 ounces) reduced fat cream cheese, softened
¼ cup reduced fat sour cream
2 cans (6 ounces each) canned crabmeat, drained and chopped
2 tablespoons lemon juice
1 teaspoon garlic, chopped fine
1 onion, chopped fine
1 tablespoon celery, chopped fine
1 tablespoon green onion, chopped fine
2 tablespoons flat parsley, chopped fine
2 teaspoons prepared mustard
1 English cucumber, sliced into ½ inch rounds

1. In a mixing bowl combine the cream cheese and sour cream until smooth.
2. Stir in the remaining ingredients. Mix until combined.
3. Put a small scoop of crabmeat onto each round of cucumber.

Makes 8 servings.   Serving size: 4 rounds.

Edita's Tip
This dip works very well with canned sardines—especially the kind packed in mustard. Just use 2 cans of the sardines in place of the crabmeat.

Sausage & Spinach Stuffed Mushrooms
(PM Fat Burner)

1 cup spinach, cooked
12 large mushrooms, stems removed
½ pound Italian sausage, without casing
½ cup onion, chopped fine
1 teaspoon garlic, chopped fine
¼ teaspoon dried thyme
¼ teaspoon dried oregano
2 tablespoons Parmesan cheese
salt and pepper to taste

Preheat oven to 375°F.
1. In a large nonstick skillet cook the sausage until heated through. Transfer to a plate.
2. In the same skillet, cook the onion, garlic until soft. Add the spinach and heat through.
3. Add the sausage back to the skillet. Mix and heat through again.
4. Place the mushrooms in a nonstick baking pan. Place a tablespoon of the mixture into each mushroom. Sprinkle with the Parmesan cheese. Bake 15 minutes. Serve hot.

Makes 6 servings.   Serving size: 2 mushrooms.

Edita's Tip
You can also sprinkle the top of these stuffed mushrooms with some chopped salted peanuts before you place them under the broiler.

Peanut Butter Smoothie
(PM Fat Burner)

½ cup nonfat vanilla yogurt
½ cup nonfat cottage cheese
4 tablespoons peanut butter, smooth
½ cup crushed ice

Combine all ingredients in a blender or food processor. Blend on high until smooth and creamy. Serve in tall glasses.

Makes 2 servings.

Peanut Butter & Jam Smoothie
(PM Fat Burner)

½ cup nonfat plain yogurt
½ cup nonfat cottage cheese
2 tablespoons strawberry jam
4 tablespoons peanut butter, smooth
½ cup crushed ice.

Combine all ingredients in a blender or food processor. Blend on high until smooth and creamy. Serve in tall glasses.

Makes 2 servings.

Thai Saté With Peanut Sauce
(PM Fat Burner)

1 pound chicken breasts, skinless & boneless
2 tablespoons peanut butter, smooth
1 tablespoon soy sauce
1 tablespoon lime or lemon juice
1 teaspoon fresh ginger, peeled and chopped fine
1 teaspoon garlic, chopped fine
2 teaspoons cilantro, chopped
8 bamboo skewers, soaked in water

Preheat oven to 450°F
1. Slice chicken into 1½ inch slices. Set aside.
2. In a blender combine the rest of the ingredients (except for the bamboo skewers) and blend until smooth.
3. Thread chicken on the skewers and place into the peanut mixture coating well. Chill for 30 minutes.
4. Remove from fridge and place on a nonstick baking sheet. Bake 10 minutes, turning occasionally. When cooked through place under broiler for 2 minutes to brown.

Makes 4 servings.   Serving size: 2 skewers.

Edita's Tip
While the chicken is cooking heat the remaining peanut sauce and use it for dipping.

Chicken & Turkey Pesto Kebabs
(PM Fat Burner)

1 pound chicken breasts, skinless and boneless
1 pound turkey breast, skinless and boneless
½ cup loosely packed fresh basil
½ cup loosely packed cilantro
¼ cup grated Parmesan cheese
1 teaspoon garlic, minced
¼ cup extra virgin olive oil
2 tablespoons lime juice
salt and pepper to taste

Preheat oven to 400°F.

1. Cut chicken and turkey into 1 ½ inch pieces.
2. In a blender or food processor combine the remaining ingredients until smooth.
3. Marinate the chicken and turkey in the pesto marinade and chill in the fridge for 30 minutes.
4. Thread alternate pieces of chicken and turkey onto metal skewers or bamboo skewers that have been soaked in water. Arrange on a nonstick cookie sheet and bake 5 to 7 minutes or until cooked.
5. Place under broiler to brown for the last 2 minutes of cooking.

Makes 6 serving.   Serving size: 2 kebabs.

Barbecued Baby Back Ribs
(PM Fat Burner)

3 pounds baby back ribs
2 cups barbecue sauce

Preheat oven to 375°F.
1. Arrange ribs in a nonstick baking pan.
2. Brush with barbecue sauce and refrigerate for 1 hour.
1. Bake for 20 to 30 minutes, basting with the barbecue sauce.
2. Serve hot with extra barbecue sauce for dipping.

Makes 4 servings.

Edita's Tip
Experiment with different barbecue sauces for a different and new dish every time.

Instant Ham & Cheese Snack
(PM Fat Burner)

2 slices of ham
2 slices of cheddar cheese, or your favorite cheese
2 slices of tomato

Arrange a slice of ham, then a slice of tomato, then a slice of cheese on a nonstick cookie sheet. Place under the broiler for a couple of minutes until the cheese melts. Enjoy. Makes 2 servings.

Chicken Gazpacho Stew
(PM Fat Burner)

6 boneless, skinless chicken breast cut into chunks
3 cans of spicy hot tomato juice
1 medium onion, chopped
2 large tomatoes, seeded and chopped
2 medium zucchini, chopped
2 tablespoons olive oil
2 tablespoons cider vinegar
1 garlic clove, minced

1. In a skillet cook chicken.
2. In a large bowl mix all ingredients, cover and refrigerate over night for 8 hours. The next day your soup will be wonderful. This is great cold or warmed up.

Makes 6 servings.

Edita's Tip
Serve this in thick bowls or cups and drop a couple of cubes of cheese into the soup for an extra zing.

Sweet and Spicy Chicken
(PM Fat Burner)

1 cup broccoli
1 cup spinach
1 cup celery, all sliced thin.
2 boneless/skinless chicken breasts, cut in small pieces
1/2 cup no sugar added apricot preserves
1 cup salsa (your favorite brand)

1. Using large skillet cook chicken pieces.
2. Then add veggies, stir well. Cook till tender crisp.
3. Add preserves and salsa, stir and heat well. Serve immediately

Makes 4 servings.

Edita's Tip
Try this dish with your favorite chutney instead of the apricot preserves to heat it up.

Surprise Packages
(PM Fat Burner)

4 boneless, skinless chicken breast halves
2 green and/or red peppers cut into strips
¼ cup tomato sauce
¼ teaspoon cracked black pepper
1/8 teaspoon ground red pepper
cooking spray

Preheat Grill
1. Coat rack with cooking spray. Pre-heat the grill.
2. Place each chicken breast in the middle of and 18"x12" piece of foil. Evenly top with peppers.
3. In a small bowl combine the tomato sauce, salt, black pepper, and red pepper until blended. Evenly drizzle over the chicken and vegetables.
4. Fold over the long sides of the foil first and bring up the ends forming a packet.
5. Place the packets, seam side up, on the rack, and grill for 25 minutes or until the vegetables are tender and a thermometer inserted in the thickest portion of a breast registers 160°F. and the juices run clear.

Makes 4 servings.

Too Easy Dinner

(PM Fat Burner)

4 skinless, boneless, chicken breasts
1 package of dried onion soup mix
2 cans of low-fat cream of chicken soup

Preheat oven 350° F

1. Sprinkle whole pack of onion soup in bottom of pan.

2. Place chicken pieces on top of dry mix. Spread soup over top of chicken evenly. Cover with tin foil and bake for approx. 45 min.

3. Take chicken out of pan and quickly mix sauce and enjoy!

Makes 4 servings.

Chuck Steak Supper
(PM Fat Burner)

2 chuck steaks
1 package dry onion soup mix
2 small cans mushrooms stems and pieces

Preheat oven to 350° F

1. Line a shallow baking pan with enough aluminum foil to seal.
2. Place chuck steaks in pan, sprinkle onion soup mix over meat and then add the mushrooms (liquid and all).
3. Seal the foil and bake for 45 minutes.

Makes: 2 servings.

Edita's Tip
I like this dish served with a big bowl of fresh green salad with a variety of lettuces and a little of your favorite reduced fat salad dressing.

Fajita Meat Loaf
(PM Fat Burner)

1 pound of lean hamburger or turkey meat
1 package of low carb fajita mix
2 egg whites
¼ cup onion, chopped fine
¼ cup carrots, shredded

Preheat oven to 350° F.
1. Mix all ingredients together and form meat into loaf.
2. Place meat loaf in the middle of your baking pan, leaving enough room around the edges for the juices to run.
3. Bake 1 hour. Slice and serve. Great cold too!

Makes 8 servings.

Edita's Tips
Try a little creamed spinach with this dish or some steamed broccoli tossed with a little olive oil and sprinkled with pine nuts.

Firecracker Salmon Steaks
(PM Fat Burner)

¼ **cup balsamic vinegar**
¼ **cup chili sauce**
1 tablespoons packed brown sugar
3 garlic cloves, minced
2 teaspoons minced fresh parsley
¼ **teaspoons ground ginger or 1 teaspoon minced fresh ginger root**
¼- ½ **teaspoon of cayenne pepper**
4 salmon steaks (6 ounces each)
cooking spray

1. In a small bowl mix the first 7 ingredients.
2. If grilling the salmon, coat the grill with non-fat cooking spray before starting the grill. Grill salmon, uncovered over medium heat or broil 4-6 inches from heat for 4-5 minutes on each side or until fish flakes easily with a fork, brushing occasionally with sauce.

Makes 4 servings.

Edita's Tip
Garnish this dish with slices of lemon and sprigs of parsley and serve it with huge platters filled with grilled vegetables such as peppers, tomatoes, zucchini and I especially like, grilled radicchio.

"Gotta' Love It" Chicken
(PM Fat Burner)

4 skinless boneless chicken breasts
3 teaspoons of brown sugar
3/4 cup of salsa
3/4 cup of tomato paste
1 tablespoon of Worcestershire sauce

Preheat oven 450° F.

Mix all ingredients. Pour over chicken in a dish. Bake for 30 minutes. Makes 4 servings

Lime-Sauced Chicken
(PM Fat Burner)

4 (4-6 oz.) fresh boneless, skinless chicken breasts
1 lime, squeezed
¾ cup 100% unsweetened apple juice
2 teaspoons cornstarch
1 chicken bouillon cube
cooking spray

Spray a large skillet with vegetable cooking spray. Heat over medium heat before adding chicken breasts. Cook for 8 to 10 minutes, or until tender, turning to brown evenly. Remove from the skillet and keep warm. In a mixing bowl combine the lime juice, apple juice, cornstarch and bouillon cube. Add to skillet and cook, stirring, until thick. Spoon sauce over chicken to serve. Makes 4 servings.

London Broil
(PM Fat Burner)

1 flank steak, about 2 lbs.
1 teaspoon olive oil
½ cup wine vinegar
1 garlic clove minced
2 teaspoons Worcestershire sauce
2 teaspoons dry mustard
½ teaspoon salt, optional
¼ teaspoon Tabasco, or hot sauce

1. Remove excess fat from steak and score.
2. Make a marinade of remaining ingredients in a large shallow pan. Marinate steaks in the refrigerator for at least 3 hours.
3. Broil each side of steaks for 3-4 minutes about 2-3 inches from heat. Slice.

Makes: 6 servings.

Edita's Tip
This steak dinner is wonderful with grilled tomatoes topped with a little Parmesan cheese and thrown under the broiler for a couple of minutes. And you could also try some lightly cooked mushrooms poured over the steak.

Poached Fish
(PM Fat Burner)

2 ½ pounds fish fillets, any kind
¼ cup finely chopped onions
1 cup tomato juice or clam juice or vegetable broth
Lemon slices

1. In large skillet, heat tomato or clam juice to boiling. Reduce heat.
2. Add fish and onion and simmer 8-10 minutes.
3. Remove with a slotted spoon.
4. Garnish with lemon.

Makes: 4 servings

Edita's Tip
Serve this with a hearty salad that includes hard-boiled egg, a few chunks of cheese, and some cooked veggies like string beans, broccoli, cauliflower or zucchini.

Veggie Chili
(PM Fat Burner)

2 pounds lean ground beef or turkey
1 green pepper, chopped
1 large onion, chopped
4 celery ribs
2 (16 oz. each) jars salsa mild, medium or hot
1 ½ cups water
1 (1.25 oz.) package low-carb taco seasoning

1. Cook beef/turkey in skillet until brown.
2. In a large pot over medium heat put, veggies, salsa, water and seasoning mix. Add meat. Cook, stirring occasionally, for 10 minutes. Serve warm.

Makes: 4 servings.

Edita's Tip
Try serving this great dish with huge leaves of Romaine lettuce or endive leaves and a big bowl of salsa for dipping.

Teriyaki Chicken
(PM Fat Burner)

1 (3 to 4 pound) chicken, cut in serving pieces
3 teaspoons white sugar
3 teaspoons brown sugar
3 teaspoons vinegar
1/2 teaspoon garlic powder
1 teaspoon ginger
1/2 cup water
1/2 cup low sodium soy sauce

Preheat oven: 350° F.
1. Arrange chicken pieces in a 9 x 13-inch baking dish.
2. Blend remaining sauce ingredients together and pour over chicken.
3. Cover tightly. Refrigerate at least 2 hours or overnight. Turn twice to marinate.
4. Bake, covered for 1 hour. Baste occasionally.

Makes 4 servings

Edita's Tip
This goes great with green beans and slivered almonds as a side dish.

Pot Roast
(PM Fat Burner)

1 tablespoon olive oil
4 pounds boneless chuck roast, trimmed of fat
1 onion, peeled and chopped
2 teaspoons garlic, minced
2 bay leaves
1 teaspoon salt
½ teaspoon pepper

Preheat oven to 325°F

1. Heat the oil in the Dutch oven over medium-high heat and sear the beef on all sides for about 3 to 4 minutes per side. Remove from pot and set aside.
2. Arrange the onion, garlic, bay leaves in the bottom of the pan and sprinkle with salt and pepper. Return the meat to the pan and cover. Bake in oven for 30 minutes. Reduce heat and cook for 1 ½ hours at 300°F. Remove and let rest for 10 minutes. Serve.

Makes 8 servings.

Edita's Tip
Leftovers are terrific for your fat burner lunch tomorrow.

Skinny Oven Omelet
(PM Fat Burner)

2 cup reduced fat cheddar cheese, shredded
1 can (4-ounces) green chilies, drained and chopped
2 cups reduced fat Monterey Jack cheese, shredded
1 ¼ cups skim milk
3 tablespoons all-purpose flour
½ teaspoon salt
¼ teaspoon white pepper
3 eggs
1 can (8-ounces) tomato sauce

Preheat oven to 350°F
1. Layer the cheddar cheese, the chilies, and the Monterey Jack cheese in the nonstick baking pan.
2. In a mixing bowl beat together the milk, flour, salt, pepper, and eggs and pour this mixture over the cheese mixture. Bake uncovered about 30 to 40 minutes or until the omelet is set in the center and the top is golden brown. Cut into squares and serve with the hot tomato sauce.

Makes 8 servings.

Edita's Tip
Save a little of this omelet for your bedtime fat burner snack to find yourself up to one pound skinnier in the morning!

Salsa Tuna Steaks
(PM Fat Burner)

1 pound tuna steaks, cut into 4 servings
2 teaspoons garlic, minced
¼ teaspoon white pepper
3 green onions, chopped
1 can (4 ounces) green chilies, chopped
1 teaspoon vegetable oil
1 tablespoon lime juice
2 tomatoes, seeded and chopped

1. Rub the tuna steaks with the pepper and ½ the garlic and place under the grill or broiler for 5 to 6 minutes. Turn repeat until the fish is flaky.
2. In a mixing bowl combine the onions, chilies, tomatoes, vegetable oil and lime juice and top the fish with the salsa mixture. Serve.

Make 4 servings.

Edita's Tip
This dish works well with salmon steaks as well and salmon is a wonderful, anti-aging, anti-wrinkle food. So go ahead, try this recipe with salmon, too.

Chicken & Oriental Vegetable Stir Fry
(PM Fat Burner)

½ cups chicken broth
1 tablespoon soy sauce
1 tablespoon cornstarch
1/8 teaspoon black pepper
2 chicken breasts, boneless, skinless ½ inch pieces
1 tablespoon vegetable oil
1 package (6 ounces) frozen snow peas, drained
1 cup mushrooms, sliced
1 red pepper, seeded and cut into ½ slices
¼ cup green onion, sliced into ½ inch pieces
1 teaspoon garlic, minced
¼ teaspoon fresh ginger, peeled and chopped fine

1. In the covered dish mix together the chicken broth, soy sauce, cornstarch and pepper. Add the chicken and toss well. Cover and chill for 1 hour.

2. In a large nonstick skillet over high heat, heat the oil. Add the snow peas, mushrooms, green onion, pepper, garlic and ginger and cook 3 to 5 minutes until tender but still crisp. Put into a bowl and set aside.

3. Add the chicken and marinade to the skillet and cook for 10 to 15 minutes, stirring occasionally, until the chicken is tender and the sauce has thickened slightly. (If the sauce gets too thick, dilute it with a little chicken broth).

4. Put the vegetables back into the skillet, mixing well and heat through and serve. Makes 4 servings.

Peppery Pork Chops
(PM Fat Burner)

4 pork chops, cut thick about 4 to 6 ounces each
2 tablespoons olive oil
½ teaspoon salt
¼ teaspoon pepper
1 cup Italian hot green peppers (peperoncini), drained
¼ cup green onions, sliced

1. Sprinkle both sides of the chops with salt and pepper.
2. Heat the oil on medium-high heat, and cook the chops until well-done and white inside. Remove from the skillet and keep warm.
3. Add the Italian peppers and onions to the pan juices, adding a little more olive oil if necessary and sauté for 3 to 4 minutes until soft. Pour the mixture over the pork chops. Serve.

Makes 4 servings.

Edita's Tip
This is best served with a cool side dish of sliced dill pickles or chilled sauerkraut sprinkled with caraway seeds.

Grilled Lemon Lamb Chops
(PM Fat Burner)

12 loin lamb chops
2 large onions, peeled and grated
¼ cup olive oil
1 lemon, halved
½ teaspoon fresh ground pepper
½ teaspoon sea salt

1. Mix the onions with the olive oil and brush over each lamb chop, both sides. Let stand for one hour.
2. Grill the chops on both sides until brown on the outside and pink inside about 5 minutes per side. Squeeze lemon juice over chops. Sprinkle with salt and pepper. Serve.

Makes 4 servings.

Edita's Tip
Serve this dish with a garlicky green salad and don't forget to toss in a little feta cheese and some olives to give it a Greek touch!

Cashew Chicken
(PM Fat Burner)

1 cup chicken broth
1 can (10 ounce) condensed cream of chicken soup
1 can (10 ounce) condensed cream of mushroom soup
2 tablespoons soy sauce
1 whole chicken, cut into pieces
1 cup cashew nuts

Preheat oven to 400°F
1. Combine the broth, soups and soy sauce in a saucepan and bring to a boil.
2. Add the chicken and ½ the cashews. Mix well and pour into the baking dish.
3. Top with the remaining nuts and bake for 20 to 30 minutes until the chicken is cooked through. Serve hot.

Makes 4 servings.

Edita's Tip
Try this with pecans, peanuts, or mixed nuts.

Balsamic Steak
(PM Fat Burner)

1 pound steak, trimmed of excess fat
1/3 cup reduced fat Italian dressing
3 tablespoons balsamic vinegar

Combine the steak, dressing, vinegar, salt and pepper in a large plastic bag and let marinate for 10 minutes. Remove steak from marinade and broil 6 inches from heat for 4 to 6 minutes per side depending on how well done you want your steak. Let stand for 5 minutes so the juices settle. Slice across the grain and serve. Makes 2 servings.

Baked Herb Chicken

(PM Fat Burner)

4 boneless, skinless chicken breast halves
2 teaspoons olive oil
6 tablespoons white wine
1/4 cup fresh lemon juice
2 teaspoons each crushed dried tarragon, basil and red pepper flakes

Preheat oven to 350°F. Brush chicken with olive oil and arrange in a shallow baking pan. Combine remaining ingredients. Pour over chicken turning several times to coat. Cover and bake until the chicken is fork tender cooked through, 25 to 30 minutes. Serve hot. Makes 4 servings.

Fish with Sun-Dried Tomatoes
(PM Fat Burner)

1 tablespoon olive oil
1 teaspoon minced garlic
1 large onion, chopped
1 cup bottled clam juice or 1 cup chicken broth
3 tablespoons oil-packed sun-dried tomatoes, chopped
1 teaspoon dried marjoram, leaves
1/2 teaspoon dried oregano, leaves
1 pound fish fillets, cut into 4 serving pieces
1 cup tomato sauce
salt and pepper to taste

1. Heat oil over medium-high heat in a 12-inch non-stick skillet.
2. Add garlic and onion. Cook, stirring, until onion is browned, about 6 minutes.
3. Stir in clam juice, sun-dried tomatoes, marjoram, and oregano. Raise heat and boil vigorously, uncovered, stirring once or twice, until liquid is reduced to about 2 tablespoons, about 4 minutes.
4. Add fish and tomato sauce and simmer 3 to 5 minutes longer until fish is cooked through and flavors are well blended. Add salt and pepper if desired.

Makes 4 servings.

Edita's Tip
This is wonderful served with a simple side of grilled vegetables brushed with a little olive oil.

Steak with Sweet Mustard
(PM Fat Burner)

4 8-ounce steaks, sirloin medallions or filet mignons
2 onions, sliced thin
1 tablespoon brown sugar
1 teaspoon reduced fat margarine
2 tablespoons red wine vinegar
2 tablespoon prepared mustard
¼ cup parsley, chopped
½ teaspoon salt

1. Place the onions in a microwave-proof container with the brown sugar, margarine, mustard, vinegar, parsley, and salt. Cover and microwave at the maximum setting for 7 minutes.
2. Transfer to a nonstick skillet and boil off any excess liquid. Keep warm.
3. Spray the skillet with cooking spray and when hot cook the steaks on medium high for 3 minutes on one side. Turn and cook for 2 minutes on the other.
4. Place the steaks on a serving platter and top with the onion mixture. Serve.

Makes 4 servings.

Edita's Tip
Try different flavors of mustard to refresh this dish again and again.

Wiener Schnitzel
(PM Fat Burner)

½ **cup all-purpose flour**
1 **teaspoon salt**
½ **teaspoon paprika**
¼ **teaspoon pepper**
4 **veal cutlets, boneless**
1 **egg**
2 **tablespoons water**
1 **cup breadcrumbs, seasoned**
cooking spray

1. Toss the flour, salt, paprika into the plastic bag and shake until mixed. Add the veal. Toss again, until the veal is coated. Remove the veal.
2. In one shallow bowl, beat the egg and water and dip the veal into the mixture.
3. In the other shallow bowl, dip the veal into the breadcrumbs.
4. Spray the pan with cooking oil and heat medium-high heat. Cook the veal about 10 minutes, turning once until tender. Serve.

Makes 4 servings.

Edita's Tip
I know you're dying to have this with potatoes or noodles.
But resist the temptation and try it with some hot
sauerkraut or icy cold coleslaw instead.

Monte Carlo Seafood Supper
(PM Fat Burner)

1 ½ pounds fish fillets, cod, halibut, etc.
1 teaspoon salt
¼ teaspoon paprika
¼ teaspoon pepper
1 green pepper, seeded and sliced into rings
1 tomato, sliced
1 onion, sliced
¼ cup olives, pitted and sliced
2 tablespoons lemon juice
1 tablespoon olive oil
1 teaspoon garlic, minced

Preheat oven to 375°F
1. Arrange the fish in the baking dish.
2. Sprinkle with salt and paprika.
3. Top with the green pepper, tomato, onion and olives.
4. Mix lemon juice, oil and garlic and pour over fish.
5. Cover and bake 15 minutes. Uncover and bake another 15 minutes or until fish flakes easily with a fork. Serve hot.

Makes 6 servings.

Edita's Tip
Serve this dish with a simple green salad and when you dress it, toss in a tablespoon or two of grated Parmesan cheese to wake up the favors of the greens.

Divine Chicken
(PM Fat Burner)

4 chicken breasts, split, boned & skin removed
1 package (10 ounces) frozen broccoli, cooked and drained
1 onion, peeled and chopped
¼ cup all purpose flour
1 ½ cups skim milk
1 teaspoon reduced-fat margarine
2 tablespoons parmesan cheese, grated
1/8 teaspoon nutmeg
cooking spray

Preheat oven to 400°F

1. Brown the chicken over medium-high heat. Remove and pat with paper towel to remove any excess fat.
2. Arrange the cooked broccoli on the bottom of a nonstick baking dish and arrange the chicken on top. Over low heat, melt the margarine in the saucepan. Add the onion, stirring. Cook 3 minutes until the onion is tender. Stir in the flour and cook for another minute. Stir in the milk, nutmeg and salt and pepper. Cook, stirring constantly until thick.
3. Pour the mixture over the chicken and broccoli. Sprinkle with the cheese and bake for 20 minutes or until bubbly. Serve hot. Makes 4 servings.

Edita's Tip
I like this dish served with a huge bowl of fresh tomatoes and onions chopped up and drizzled with balsamic vinegar.

Hot & Hearty Stew
(PM Fat Burner)

1 pound chicken breasts, skinless, cut into chunks
1 pound turkey breast, skinless, cut into chunks
1 can chicken broth
1 can cream of mushroom soup
1 cup celery, sliced
1 cup onion, peeled and chopped

Preheat oven to 375°F
1. Combine all the ingredients in the casserole and bake for 1 hour until the stew bubbles and the meat is tender. Serve hot.

Makes 8 servings.

Edita's Tip
Pour this stew over some freshly cooked spaghetti squash seasoned with a little olive oil and freshly ground pepper.

Family Favorite Sloppy Joes
(PM Fat Burner)

1 pound ground beef
1 (12 ounce) jar chili sauce
2 tablespoons brown sugar
½ teaspoon salt
¼ teaspoon pepper

Preheat broiler.
1. In a large, nonstick skillet, brown the beef over medium-high heat about 5 to 6 minutes, stirring until all the meat is evenly browned.
2. Add the chili sauce, and brown sugar and cook another 2 minutes.
3. Mix in the salt and pepper.
4. Spoon the beef mixture into bowls. Serve hot.

Makes 4 servings.

Edita's Tip
Try scooping up this wonderful mixture with crunchy slices of zucchini.

Viennese Stuffed Cabbage
(PM Fat Burner)

1 head of cabbage
2 onions, chopped fine
2 tablespoons margarine
1 teaspoon paprika
2 cups leftover cooked beef, chopped fine
¼ cup parsley, chopped fine
½ teaspoon rosemary and ½ teaspoon dried garlic
1 16-ounce can tomatoes, drained and chopped
¾ cup meat sauce or carbonara sauce

Preheat oven to 350°F.

1. Place the head of cabbage in a large bowl and pour boiling water over it to loosen the leaves. Drop 8 of the largest outer leaves into a large pot of boiling salted water and cook for 2-4 minutes. Lift out using a slotted spoon and drain on paper towels. Cut a v-shape in each leaf to remove the hard stem.
2. In a skillet sauté the onions and margarine. In a large bowl combine the remaining ingredients. Reserving ½ the sauce and all the tomatoes.
3. Pour the onion over the mixture. Combine well. Place 1/8 of the filling into the center of each of the cabbage leaves. Roll up and secure with toothpick.
4. Arrange the stuffed cabbage leaves, seam-side down in a non-stick casserole. Pour the tomatoes over the cabbage leaves. Top with the meat sauce.
5. Cover and bake for 50-60 minutes. Serve hot.

Makes 8 servings.

Dinner Salad Platter
(PM Fat Burner)

1 head boston lettuce leaves
6 leaves, curly endive
1 can 3-ounces canned red salmon, drained and flaked
1 can 3 ½ ounces tuna packed in water, drained and flaked
½ cup nonfat ranch dressing
1 tablespoon green onion, chopped fine
1 cucumber, sliced fine
8 olives, drained
8 slices cooked chicken breast
8 slices honey-roasted ham slices
½ pound green beans, cooked and cut into julienne strips
2 tomatoes, sliced
2 hard cooked egg, peeled and halved

1. Line a large platter with the boston lettuce leaves.
2. Arrange the cucumber, olives, chicken, ham, green beans, tomato slices, egg halves, and potatoes around the outer edges of the platter leaving room in the center.
3. Line the center of the platter with curly endive.
4. In a small bowl mix the tuna, salmon and green onion together with the ranch dressing.
   Makes 4 servings.

Edita's Tip
Scoop the mixture onto the endive in the center of the platter.

Martha's Vineyard Seafood Supper
(PM Fat Burner)

1 ½ pounds fish fillets, cod, halibut, etc.
1 teaspoon salt
¼ teaspoon paprika
¼ teaspoon pepper
1 green pepper, seeded and sliced into rings
1 tomato, sliced
1 onion, sliced
¼ cup olives, pitted and sliced
2 tablespoons lemon juice
1 tablespoon olive oil
1 teaspoon garlic, minced

Preheat oven to 375°F.
1. Arrange the fish in a non-stick baking dish.
2. Sprinkle with salt and paprika.
3. Top with the green pepper, tomato, onion and olives.
4. Mix lemon juice, oil and garlic and pour over fish. Cover and bake 15 minutes.
5. Uncover and bake another 15 minutes or until fish flakes easily with a fork.

Makes 6 servings.

Edita's Tip
Fish is one of the best fat-burners we have. Enjoy every skinny bite and know that you are burning fat pounds and fat inches with every mouthful.

French Tomato Omelet
(PM Fat Burner)

2 cups reduced fat cheddar cheese, shredded
1 can (4-ounces) green chilies, drained and chopped
2 cups reduced fat Monterey Jack cheese, shredded
1 ¼ cups skim milk
3 tablespoons all-purpose flour
½ teaspoon salt
¼ teaspoon white pepper
8 eggs
1 can (8-ounces) tomato sauce

Preheat oven to 350°F.
1. Layer the cheddar cheese, the chilies, and cheese in a nonstick baking pan.
2. In a mixing bowl beat together the milk, flour, salt, pepper, and eggs and pour this mixture over the cheese mixture.
3. Bake uncovered about 10 to 15 minutes or until the omelet is set in the center and the top is golden brown.
4. Cut into squares and serve with the hot tomato sauce.

Makes 8 servings.

San Miguel Hot Beef Salad
(PM Fat Burner)

2 cups onion, chopped fine
1 teaspoon garlic powder
1 20-ounce can seasoned tomatoes, chopped and drained
1 pound lean ground beef
1 green pepper, seeded and chopped
1 yellow pepper, seeded and chopped
2 tablespoons chili powder
1 tablespoon cumin
1/8 teaspoon crushed red peppers
salt and pepper to taste
cooking spray

1. Sautee the onion, garlic powder, and the tomatoes in a skillet until the onions are tender about 5 minutes. Remove.
2. In the same skillet brown the beef. Cook for 5 more minutes or until the beef is well cooked through and through. Drain the mixture well.
3. Add the two mixtures together and combine.
4. Serve with shredded low fat cheddar cheese, sliced lettuce, and salsa.

Makes 4 servings.

Late Supper Chicken Salad

(PM Fat Burner)

2 cups cooked chicken, chopped
1 cup spinach leaves, torn into bits
1 red pepper, seeded and chopped
1 green pepper, seeded and chopped
¼ cup plain yogurt
¼ cup mayo
1 clove garlic, minced
¼ teaspoon rosemary
4 large leaves Romaine lettuce

1. In a large bowl combine all ingredients. Toss well to coat.
2. Cover and chill for 2 hours. Place a leaf of the Romaine lettuce on each of 4 salad plates. Arrange the salad on top, dividing equally among the plates. Makes 4 servings.

A Little Soul Food
Whenever you fall, pick something up.

Spinach & Cheese Pie
(PM Fat Burner)

2 cups sliced fresh mushrooms
2 tbsp water
2 packages (10 oz. ea.) chopped spinach
2 cups evaporated skim milk
2 cups fat-free egg substitute
2 cups shredded reduced-fat mozzarella cheese
¼ cup minced fresh parsley
1 tsp crushed fresh garlic
1 tsp dried thyme
¼ cup grated nonfat or reduced-fat Parmesan cheese

Preheat oven to 375°F.

1. Place the mushrooms and water in a 3-quart pot. Cook and stir over medium heat until the mushrooms are tender and the liquid has evaporated.
2. Remove the pot from the heat, and stir in first the spinach; then the evaporated milk, and the egg substitute, mozzarella cheese, parsley, garlic, thyme, and pepper.
3. Divide the pie filling evenly between the two nonstick baking pans and top each of the filled pies with half of the Parmesan cheese.
4. Bake for 45 minutes, or until a sharp knife inserted in the center of each pie comes out clean.
5. Remove the pies from the oven and let sit for 5 minutes before cutting into wedges and serving.

Makes 6 servings.

Steamed Clams
(PM Fat Burner)

5 dozen clams
1 cup water
4 garlic cloves, peeled and chopped
2 onions, chopped fine
2 bay leaves
1 teaspoon dried thyme
6 peppercorns

1. Scrub clams to remove sand and bring to a boil with all remaining ingredients.
2. Cook for 5 to 10 minutes or until clams open.
3. Strain broth and serve on the side in individual bowls for dipping the clams.

Makes 4 servings.

Edita's Tip
I like to sprinkle a little balsamic vinegar into the broth or add a dab of wasabi.

Bedtime Baked Eggs
(PM Fat Burner)

4 eggs
1 cup spinach leaves, washed and torn into bite-size bits
salt and pepper to taste
½ cup grated cheddar cheese

1. Line four small oven-proof bowls with the spinach leaves and sprinkle with salt and pepper.
2. Break an egg into each bowl on top of the spinach.
3. Bake for 12 minutes and top with cheese, returning to oven for another 3 minutes until the cheese melts and the eggs are cooked.

Makes 4 servings.

Ranch Nuts
(PM Fat Burner)

1 cup each peanuts, cashews, walnuts and pecans
¼ cup reduced fat Ranch dressing
1 envelope Ranch salad dressing mix

Preheat oven to 300°F.
In a mixing bowl combine all the ingredients. Stir to mix well. Spread evenly on a nonstick cookie sheet. Bake for 30 minutes or until lightly browned. Cool.

Makes 8 servings.   Serving size: ½ cup

Chimichurri
(PM Fat Burner)

1 pound beef tenderloin, cut into ½ cubes
1 tablespoon olive oil
2 tablespoons oregano
2 tablespoons fresh parsley, chopped fine
2 tablespoons garlic, chopped fine
1 teaspoon paprika
1 teaspoon salt
1 teaspoon crushed red pepper flakes
½ teaspoon ground black pepper
½ teaspoon ground white pepper
4 wooden skewers soaked in water

Preheat broiler or grill.
1. Combine all the ingredients in a large plastic bag. Toss to coat well. Chill for 24 hours.
2. Skewer the meat on the wooden skewers or on metal ones and grill for 7 to 10 minutes until cooked the way you like them. Serve hot or cold.

Makes 4 servings

Serving size: 1 skewer

Meat Sticks
(PM Fat Burner)

24 pieces of beef or chicken cut into strips
6 wooded skewers, soaked in water
salt and pepper
4 cups salsa

Preheat broiler.
1. Use 4 pieces of meat per skewer, leaving space between each piece. Season with salt and pepper.
2. Place on nonstick broiler tray and broil for 7 to 10 minutes, turning once, until meat is cooked.
3. Serve with salsa for dipping.

Makes 6 servings.   Serving size: 1 skewer

Stuffed Avocado
(PM Fat Burner)

2 avocados, cut in half and seeded
1 can (6 ounces) tuna packed in water and drained
1 cup nonfat cottage cheese
2 tablespoons lemon juice
salt and pepper

In a mixing bowl combine the tuna, cottage cheese, lemon juice. Add salt and pepper to taste. Fill the four avocado halves with the tuna mixture. Serve. Makes 4 servings. Serving size: ½ avocado

Peanut Butter & Jam Dip
(PM Fat Burner)

1 package (8 ounces) reduced fat cream cheese
1 ½ cups peanut butter, creamy or chunky
1 tablespoon skim milk
¼ cup strawberry jam

In a mixing bowl combine all the ingredients. Dip celery, veggies or spread on chunks of your favorite cheese.

Makes 16 servings.   Serving size: 2 teaspoons

Peanut Bacon Stuffers
(PM Fat Burner)

1 cup peanut butter, smooth or crunchy
8 slices bacon, cooked crisp, crumbled
24 pieces of celery, 2 inches each

1. In a mixing bowl combine the peanut butter and bacon.
2. Fill the celery with the peanut butter mixture.

Makes 24 servings.   Serving size: 4 pieces

Sweet Peanut Butter Cups
(PM Fat Burner)

1 cup peanut butter, crunchy
1 package (8 ounces) cream cheese, softened
½ cup skim milk
½ cup powdered sugar
1 teaspoon cinnamon
1 carton (8 ounces) nonfat whipped topping

1. Blend the peanut butter, cream cheese, milk, sugar, and cinnamon together.
2. Fold in the whipped topping.
3. Divide into 8 dessert cups. Chill. Serve.

Makes 8 servings.

Spicy Pecans
(PM Fat Burner)

1 pound pecan halves, without shells
1 egg white, slightly beaten
2 tablespoons ground cinnamon
1 teaspoon nutmeg
½ cup sugar

Preheat oven to 325°F.
1. In a plastic bag, combine the pecans, egg white, spices and sugar until well coated.
2. Bake on a nonstick cookie sheet for 20 minutes. Cool.

Mini Italian Frittatas
(PM Fat Burner)

6 eggs, lightly beaten
1 ½ cups half-half
½ teaspoon freshly ground black pepper
¼ cup cooked bacon, crumbled
¼ cup grated cheddar cheese

Preheat oven to 350°F.
1. In a mixing bowl whisk together all the ingredients.
2. Divide mixture into 12 nonstick muffin cups and bake for 20 to 30 minutes or until the eggs are firm.

Makes 6 servings.

Edita's Tip
Remember, it is the protein you eat at bedtime that will keep your body burning fat all night long for a skinny sleep.

Chopped Sweet Ham Salad
(PM Fat Burner)

3 cups cooked ham, chopped fine
½ cup celery, chopped fine
1 bunch green onions, chopped fine
½ cup green pepper, seeded and chopped
1/3 cup sweet pickle relish
1 teaspoon mustard
½ cup reduced fat mayonnaise

1. In a mixing bowl combine the ham, celery, onions, peppers and relish.
2. Add the mustard and mayonnaise and mix well.
3. Chill for one hour. Serve.

Makes 8 servings.

Edita's Tip
I love to just spoon up a couple of spoonfuls of this wonderful nighttime salad.

Bedtime Chicken Snack
(PM Fat Burner)

3 cups cooked chicken, cubed
2/3 cups celery chopped fine
1 bunch green onions, chopped fine
2 eggs, hard boiled and chopped fine
½ cup reduced fat mayonnaise
¼ cup nonfat yogurt, plain

1. In a mixing bowl combine the chicken, celery, green onions and the egg and toss to mix well.
2. Add the mayonnaise and yogurt and mix until completely coated.
3. Chill for one hour. Serve.

Makes 8 servings.   Serving size: ½ cup

Bacon Chestnut Wraps
(PM Fat Burner)

1 can (8 ounces) whole water chestnuts, drained
½ pound bacon, each strip cut into thirds

Preheat oven to 375°F.
1. Wrap a 1/3 slice of bacon around each water chestnut and fasten with a toothpick.
2. Place in a single layer on a nonstick cookie sheet and bake for 20 minutes or until bacon is crisp.
3. Drain on paper towels. Serve hot.

Makes about 24 pieces.   Serving size: 3 pieces

Spicy Chicken Wings
(PM Fat Burner)

12 chicken wings
¼ cup margarine, melted
¼ cup honey
¼ cup prepared mustard
1 teaspoon chili powder
½ teaspoon garlic powder

Preheat oven to 325°F.

1. Prepare the chicken wings by cutting off the wingtips and cutting the actual wing in half at the joint.
2. In a large plastic bag combine the margarine, honey, mustard and spices. Add the chicken wings and toss to coat well. Remove the chicken wings.
3. Bake the chicken wings on a nonstick cookie sheet for 1 hour. Serve hot.

Makes 4 servings.   Serving size: 3 wings

Edita's Tip
Dip these in a little honey for an extra touch of sweetness.

Chocolate Peanut Butter Brownies
(Carb Attack)

1 16-ounce package brownie mix
1 cup peanut butter morsels
½ cup peanuts, chopped

Preheat oven to 350°F.
1. In a medium bowl prepare the brownie mix according to package directions.
2. Add the peanut butter morsels and chopped peanuts. Mix until smooth.
3. Pour batter into a 13 x 9 inch nonfat baking pan coated with cooking spray. Bake for 30 minutes or until the brownie begins to pull away from the edges of the pan. Cool on a wire rack. Cut into squares.

Makes 24 servings.   Serving size: 1 brownie

Edita's Tip
Try making this recipe with walnuts or pecans and for a fancier presentation dust the top of the brownies with powdered sugar. Remember to take my Skinny Carbs to help you not gain any additional fat pounds.

Chocoholics Cookies
(Carb Attack)

1 cup sweetened condensed milk
4 cups coconut, shredded
1 cup semi-sweet chocolate chips
1 teaspoon vanilla
1 teaspoon almond extract

Preheat oven to 325°F.
1. Combine all the ingredients in a mixing bowl and stir until well blended.
2. Drop by teaspoons onto a nonstick baking sheet and bake for 10 to 15 minutes. Enjoy.

Makes 24 cookies   Serving size: 2 cookies

Edita's Tip
These cookies taste wonderful if you switch out the chocolate chips for butterscotch chips and substitute the almond extract for butterscotch flavoring.

S'Mores
(Carb Attack)

16 graham crackers
8 squares of chocolate
24 miniature marshmallows

1. Place 8 graham crackers on a large microwave safe paper plate.
2. Top each cracker with 1 square of chocolate and 3 miniature marshmallows.
3. Microwave on high for 3 minutes or until the marshmallows begin to puff up.
4. Top each cracker with the remaining crackers.

Makes 8 servings.   Serving size: 1 S'More

Edita's Tip
If anything will make you feel like a kid again, these will.
Get the whole family involved in making these treats.

Corn Flake Cookies
(Carb Attack)

1 cup margarine, softened
1 cup granulated sugar
2/3 cups brown sugar
2 eggs, beaten
1 teaspoon vanilla
½ cup peanut butter
2 cups all-purpose flour
1 teaspoon baking powder
1 teaspoon baking soda
4 cups corn flakes
1 ½ cups jelly beans, chopped

Preheat oven to 350°F.
1. In a mixing bowl, combine the margarine and sugars.
2. Add the eggs, vanilla, and peanut butter. Mix until well blended.
3. In a separate bowl, combine the flour, baking powder, and baking soda.
4. Stir the dry mixture into the margarine mixture.
5. Stir in the cereal and candies.
6. Drop by rounded teaspoonfuls about 2 inches apart onto a nonstick baking sheet sprayed with cooking spray.
7. Bake 8 to 10 minutes or until golden brown. Cool 1 minute. Remove from baking sheet with a spatula. Cool on wire rack.

Makes 48 servings.   Serving size: 1 cookie.

Chocolate Bars
(Carb Attack)

1/3 cup margarine
¼ cup corn syrup
1 ½ cup pancake mix
1 ½ oatmeal, uncooked
½ cup sugar
½ cup walnuts
1 cup chocolate chips
1 egg

Preheat oven to 300°F.
1. In a small saucepan, melt the margarine and syrup over medium-low heat.
2. Mix the remaining ingredients in a large bowl, reserving the egg.
3. Stir in the margarine mixture and the egg.
4. Combine until all the dry ingredients are moistened.
5. Place in a nonstick baking pan 13x9x2 and smooth. Bake for 30 to 35 minutes until golden brown. Remove from oven and cut into bars. Cool in pan for 30 minutes.

Makes 40 servings.   Serving size: 1 bar.

Edita's Tip
Oatmeal never tasted this good!

Almond Biscotti
(Carb Attack)

1 cup flour
1 cup whole wheat flour
2/3 cup sugar
2 teaspoons baking powder
4 tablespoons margarine
3 egg whites
1 teaspoon vanilla extract, and 1 of almond extract
½ teaspoon finely chopped almonds

Preheat oven to 350°F.

1. In a mixing bowl combine the flour, sugar and baking powder and mix well.
2. With a pastry cutter or two forks cut the margarine into the mixture until it resembles coarse meal.
3. Stir in the egg whites and the vanilla and almond extract. Fold in the almonds.
4. Turn the dough onto a lightly floured surface and shape into two 9 x 2-inch logs.
5. Place the logs on a nonstick baking sheet, not too close together. Bake for 25 minutes or until lightly browned. Cool the logs for 10 minutes.
6. Slice diagonally into ½-inch-thick slices. Place the slices on a clean nonstick baking sheet in a single layer, cut side down. Bake at the same oven temperature for 18 to 20 minutes or until the slices are dry and crisp. Turn once after the first 10 minutes. Cool on a wire rack.

Makes 24 servings.   Serving size: 1 biscotti

Rum Balls
(Carb Attack)

3 cups finely crushed vanilla wafers
2 cups powdered sugar
1 cup finely chopped walnuts
¼ cup cocoa
¼ cup light corn syrup
1 teaspoon rum flavoring
½ cup chopped coconut
water or skim milk

1. Mix all ingredients together.
2. Add a little water or skim milk by teaspoonfuls until the consistency is that which will allow you to form the mixture into balls.
3. Roll the balls in the coconut. Place in an airtight container and keep in the fridge for 24 hours before serving.

Makes 60.   Serving size: 2

Edita's Tip
This was a favorite holiday dessert when I was growing up. We used to roll the coconut balls in sugar, sprinkles and cocoa for variety.

Poached Pears In Coconut
(Carb Attack)

2 cups coconut milk
1/3 cup sugar
1 cinnamon stick
4 pears, peeled and halved

1. Place the coconut milk, sugar and cinnamon in a nonstick saucepan over medium-low heat. Do not allow the milk to boil.
2. Add the pears and simmer for 15 minutes, turning once.
3. Place a pear into the bottom of a dessert bowl and top with some of the milk.

Makes 4 servings.

Edita's Tip
Try different varieties of pears to give this warm wonderful dessert a fresh look and taste each time.

Hot Strawberry Shortcakes
(Carb Attack)

1 pound strawberries, washed and hulled
¼ cup sugar
4 large sugar cookies or shortbread biscuits
vanilla ice cream or frozen yogurt

1. Pour the sugar onto a plate and roll the strawberries in it until well coated.
2. Cook the strawberries for 2 minutes in a nonstick skillet on high heat until warmed and the sugar coating is melted. Remove the strawberries and set aside.
3. Place the cookies or biscuits on individual dessert plates top with the warm strawberries and a little of the melted sugar sauce from the pan. Serve with a scoop of ice cream or frozen yogurt.

Makes 4 servings.

Edita's Tip
I love this with raspberries, blueberries, or blackberries!

Sugar Roasted Red Fruit
(Carb Attack)

2 nectarines, halved and pitted
4 plums, halved and pitted
12 red grapes, halved and pitted
3 tablespoons sugar

Preheat oven to 425°F.

1. Place the fruit in a nonstick baking pan and sprinkle with the sugar.
2. Bake for 20 minutes or until the sugar is golden. Serve with a scoop of frozen yogurt or vanilla ice cream.

Makes 4 servings.

Edita's Tip
There is something so satisfying about hot fruit paired with icy cold frozen yogurt or ice cream. Or try this as a topper for pancakes or waffles. Enjoy!

Strawberry Mousse
(Carb Attack)

2 cups strawberries, washed, hulled and quartered
½ cup nonfat sour cream
4 to 5 packets artificial sweetener
1½ cups nonfat, frozen whipped topping, slightly thawed

1. Place the strawberries and the artificial sweetener in the blender or food processor and process until smooth.
2. Transfer the mixture to a large mixing bowl and mix in the sour cream.
3. Fold in the whipped topping. Divide equally among the six dessert cups, cover and freeze for 4 hours. Serve frozen.

Makes 6 servings.

Edita's Tip
Garnish the dessert cups with slices of strawberries and serve with ginger snaps or vanilla wafers.

Cheese Cake Parfait
(Carb Attack)

4 cups plain, nonfat yogurt
1 cup nonfat cottage cheese
4 to 6 packets artificial sweetener
2 tablespoons all-purpose flour
1 tablespoon lemon juice
1 teaspoon vanilla

1. Spoon the yogurt into a large strainer lined with a coffee filter. Place a bowl beneath the strainer, but not touching the bottom of the strainer to catch liquid. Chill 24 hours and discard the liquid.
2. Process the cottage cheese in a blender or food processor until smooth. Add the drained yogurt, sweetener, lemon juice and vanilla. Process again, until well blended.
3. Divide among 6 tall glasses. Chill and serve.

Makes 8 servings.

Edita's Tip
The yogurt cheese in this recipe has endless variations. Try it mixed with nuts, chopped meats, chopped veggies or flavored with your favorite spices as a dip.

Comfort Pudding
(Carb Attack)

1 package gelatin, strawberry flavored
1 cup nonfat yogurt, strawberry

Prepare the gelatin according to package directions. Chill until it begins to set. Stir in the yogurt. Mix well. Chill until set. Serve. Makes 4 servings.

Edita's Tip
Try different flavor combinations: Lemon, cherry, vanilla, tropical fruit. This is true comfort food that's also good for you.

Pink Peach Sorbet
(Carb Attack)

1 package (16-ounces) peach slices, frozen
4-6 packets artificial sweetener
¼ cup lemon juice
2-3 drops red food coloring
1 tablespoon almond flavoring

In the bowl of a food processor, combine the peaches, sweetener, lemon juice and flavoring. Puree until smooth. Spoon into dessert cups and serve. Makes 4 servings.

Baby Kisses
(Carb Attack)

1 package (16 ounces) angel food cake mix
½ cup water
1 teaspoon almond extract
2 cups coconut, flaked

Preheat oven to 350°F.
1. Prepare cake according to package directions adding the water and almond extract.
2. Fold in the coconut.
3. Drop by teaspoons onto a nonstick cookie sheet and bake for 10 to 12 minutes. Cool on wire rack.

Makes 24 servings.   Serving size: 2

Edita's Tip
I like to have a couple of these as my mid-morning fat blocker AM snack when I really crave something sweet and special.

Heavy Fruit Cake Loaf
(Carb Attack)

1 (15 ounce) package cranberry quick bread mix
1 cup fresh or frozen cranberries
½ cup currents
½ cup raisins
½ cup pecans, chopped
½ cup dates, chopped
½ cup maraschino cherries, drained and chopped
½ cup pineapple, crushed and drained

Preheat oven to 350°F.
1. Prepare the bread according to package directions. Add the remaining ingredients. Pour into a nonstick loaf pan.
2. Bake for 45 to 60 minutes or until a toothpick inserted into the loaf comes out clean. Cool.

Makes 12 servings.

Edita's Tip
I love this bread for breakfast. I just pop a slice into my microwave to warm it up for a few seconds and I've got one of the best breakfasts!

Cheesecake
(Carb Attack)

2 packages (8 ounces each) reduced fat cream cheese, softened
½ cup sugar
1 teaspoon vanilla
2 eggs
1 (9 inch) graham cracker pie crust

Preheat oven to 350°F.

1. With an electric mix blend together the cheese, sugar, vanilla and eggs until smooth and creamy.
2. Pour into prepared pie crust and bake for 40 to 45 minutes. Cool.

Makes 8 servings.

Edita's Tip

This is one of my favorite fast desserts. I top it off with a big spoonful of frozen whipped topping and a few chocolate sprinkles. It's like your basic black dress. Dress it up. Dress it down. You'll be able to find your own favorite ways to serve this fast and simple cheesecake.

The Cobbler
(Carb Attack)

2 cans strawberry, blueberry, or cherry pie filling
½ cup raisins
1 package white or yellow cake mix
2 sticks margarine, melted

Preheat oven to 350°F.

1. Spread the pie filling on the bottom of a nonstick 13 x 9-inch baking pan.
2. Sprinkle the cake mix over the pie filling and drizzle the margarine over the top.
3. Bake for 50 to 60 minutes until hot and bubbly.

Makes 8 servings.

Edita's Tip
Vanilla ice cream goes great with this wonderful, warm and sweet dessert. Try making it with crushed pineapple or hot cooked apples. I serve it to company in flat champagne glasses and it looks and tastes like a million!

Trifle Parfait
(Carb Attack)

1 (12 ounce) pound cake, cut into ½ inch slices
1/3 cup pineapple juice
2 cans cherry pie filling
2 cups strawberries, sliced
2 cups bananas, sliced
4 cups vanilla pudding
1 carton (8 ounces) frozen dessert topping

1. Line the bottom of a large trifle bowl with pound cake and brush with pineapple juice.
2. Top with 1/3 of the pie filling, then 1/3 of the strawberries, 1/3 of the bananas, and 1/3 of the pudding
3. Repeat the layers. Top with the frozen dessert. Chill 2 hours and serve.

Edita's Tip
It doesn't matter what you use for a trifle. The secret is in soaking the cake layer and then alternating layers with fruit and pudding. I always serve this in a huge glass bowl because it looks so terrific!

Rice Krispie Crunchies With Nuts
(Carb Attack)

1 stick margarine, melted
2 cups peanut butter, crunchy
1 (16 ounce) box powdered sugar
3 ½ cups Rice Krispies
¾ cups chopped peanuts

1. Mix the melted margarine and peanut butter in a large mixing bowl.
2. Add the sugar, cereal, and peanuts and mix well.
3. Drop by teaspoons on a nonstick cookie sheet. Chill 2 hours. Serve.

Makes 24 servings.

Edita's Tip
Go ahead. Be a kid again. I always loved Rice Krispie squares and this is a great variation I found when I was experimenting with different ways to enjoy peanut butter.

Fudge, Fudge, Fudge
(Carb Attack)

3 cups semisweet chocolate chips
1 can sweetened condensed milk
½ stick margarine, melted
1 cup chopped nuts

1. In a microwave safe bowl mix together the chocolate, milk and margarine and microwave on medium for 5 minutes, stirring often.
2. Stir in the nuts and pour into a nonstick 8-inch square fudge pan. Chill for 2 hours and cut into squares.

Makes 12 servings.

Edita's Tip
This may not be the best candy store fudge, but believe me, when you crave rich chocolate candy, fast...this is melt-in-your-mouth, delicious!

Super Sticky Gooey Dessert Muffins
(Carb Attack)

1 cup applesauce
½ cup finely chopped dried apricots
1 ¾ cups all-purpose flour
1/3 cup uncooked farina
1/3 cup artificial sweetener
2 teaspoons baking powder
1/8 teaspoon ground nutmeg
1 teaspoon vanilla extract
3 large egg whites, lightly beaten
1 (8 ounce) container plain fat-free yogurt
2 tablespoons sugar

Preheat oven to 400°F.

1. Combine applesauce and apricots in a microwave-safe bowl. Cover with plastic wrap. Microwave at high 3 minutes or until mixture boils. Cool. Drain apricots in a colander over a bowl, reserving apple juice.

2. Combine flour and the next 5 ingredients and make well in a center of mixture. Whisk 3 tablespoons reserved applesauce, vanilla, egg whites, and yogurt. Add to flour mixture, stirring just until moist. Stir in reserved apricots.

3. Spoon batter into 12 muffin cups lined with paper muffin cups. Bake 20 minutes. Dip muffin tops in remaining applesauce; sprinkle each with ½ teaspoon sweetener.

Makes 12 muffins.   Serving size: 1 muffin

Carrot Cupcakes
(Carb Attack)

1 ¾ cups all-purpose flour
½ cup sugar
½ cup oat bran
1 teaspoon baking soda
1 teaspoon allspice
1 teaspoon nutmeg
½ teaspoon baking powder
2 cups carrots, peeled and shredded
2 eggs
½ cup each applesauce and raisins

Preheat oven to 350°F
1. Line the muffin tins with paper muffin cups.
2. In a medium bowl combine the flour, sugar, oat bran, spices, baking soda, and baking powder.
3. In another bowl mix the carrots, eggs, applesauce and raisins.
4. Stir flour mixture into the carrot mixture until the flour is moistened and spoon into muffin cups about 2/3 full.
5. Bake for 30 minutes or until a toothpick inserted in the center comes out clean. Ice with your favorite frosting or top with whipped topping.

Makes 12 cupcakes   Serving size: 1 cupcake

Edita's Tip
Turn these into your favorite holiday cupcakes by simply substituting the carrots for pumpkin or yams!

Sweet Spoons
(Carb Attack)

24 plastic spoons
1 cup white chocolate pieces
1 cup semi sweet chocolate pieces
Assorted sprinkles

1. In a nonstick saucepan melt the white chocolate.
2. In a second nonstick saucepan melt the dark chocolate
3. Dip each spoon into one or the other of the melted chocolates twice for a full-coated effect or swirl spoons into both.
4. Cool on waxed paper. Use to stir your coffee or to scoop up your favorite dessert, or just enjoy licking each spoon for a sweet treat.

Makes 18 spoons.   Serving size: 1 spoon

Candy Pizzas
(Carb Attack)

48 vanilla wafers
1 tub chocolate frosting
2 cups of your favorite candies, jelly beans, gum drops, chocolate chips, cinnamon hearts, caramel pieces, shredded coconut, sprinkles, etc.

1. Spread frosting on cookies and decorate with your favorite candies and toppings. Enjoy. Makes 48 pieces. Serving size: 2 cookies

Peanut Butter & Jelly Cookies
(Carb Attack)

½ cup sugar, white
½ cup sugar, brown
½ cup peanut butter, smooth or crunchy
¼ cup margerine
¼ cup applesauce
1 egg
1 ¼ cups flour
¾ teaspoon baking soda
½ teaspoon baking powder
1 cup strawberry jam or jelly

Preheat oven to 375°F.

1. In a large mixing bowl beat together the sugars, peanut butter, margarine, and egg until combined. Stir in the flour, baking soda and baking power. Chill for 3 hours or until firm.
2. Shape into 1-inch balls and place on nonstick cookie sheet. Flatten with the back of a fork.
3. Bake 10 minutes until golden. Cool on wire rack. Spread jam or jelly between the bottoms of two cookies to make a sandwich.

Makes 18 cookie sandwiches   Serving size: 1 sandwich

Fireside Rice Pudding
(Carb Attack)

4 cups skim milk
1 cup rice, quick-cooking, long-grain
½ cup raisins
1 package (1 ounce) vanilla pudding and pie filling
2 egg whites
½ teaspoon rum extract (almond extract works well)

In a nonstick saucepan combine all the ingredients and
bring to a boil, stirring constantly. Reduce heat and simmer
5 minutes. Remove from heat. Serve.

Makes 8 servings.   Serving size: ½ cup

Sweet Snacks
(Carb Attack)

1 cup animal crackers
1 cup graham crackers, broken into pieces
1 cup raisins
1 cup M&M®s
1 cup honey roasted peanuts

Combine all the ingredients in a large plastic bag. Toss
until well mixed. Serve.

Makes 6 servings.   Serving size: 1 cup

Chocolate Coffee Mousse
(Carb Attack)

1 carton (12 ounce) nonfat whipped topping
2 teaspoons instant coffee, dry
5 teaspoons cocoa
2 tablespoons rum extract

In a mixing bowl, combine the whipped topping, coffee, cocoa and rum extract until completely blended. Serve.

Makes 4 servings.

Brownies With Bits
(Carb Attack)

1 package prepared brownie mix
1 cup chocolate chips or peanut butter morsels

Preheat oven to 350°F.
1. Prepare brownies according to package directions, stirring in the chocolate chips or peanut butter morsels.
2. Bake for 30 to 40 minutes. Cool. Cut into squares.

Makes 12 brownies.   Serving size: 1 brownie

Golden Pineapple Cakes
(Carb Attack)

1 box yellow cake mix
4 eggs
⅓ cup vegetable oil
⅔ cups applesauce
1 can (14 ounces) crushed pineapple with juice

Preheat oven to 350°F.
1. Beat together all the ingredients with an electric mixer or in a food processor.
2. Pour into paper lined muffin tins, ¾ full. Bake for 30 to 35 minutes or until a toothpick inserted in the center comes out clean. Cool.

Makes 12 servings.   Serving size: 1 individual cake

Skinny Strawberry Shortcake
(Carb Attack)

1 prepared angel food cake
3 cups fresh strawberries, washed, hulled and sliced
1 tub (8 ounces) nonfat whipped dessert topping

1. Place the cake on a cake plate.
2. Put generous dollops of the dessert topping on top of the cake and around the sides.
3. Sprinkle with strawberries. Serve.

Makes 6 servings.

Resources

The Skinny Foods—Master List

Here is a master list of approved Skinny Foods that will help you keep winning your fat fight once you are ready to strike out on your own and put your own skinny meals together. But this is only if you have reached your skinny goal. If not, stay with my 2-day, or 5-day programs until you reach your goals.

Fat Blocking AM Foods

Apples
Artichoke
Animal crackers
Brussels sprouts
Baked beans
Broccoli
Broad beans
Bread crumbs
Bagels
Bread, whole wheat
Beans
Cream of wheat
Carob flour
Cookies, fig
Chicory
Coconut
Corn flour
Cranberries
Currants
Cauliflower
Dandelion greens

Applesauce
Asparagus

Bulgar
Beet greens
Black berries
Bread, white
Bread, 7-grain
Bread, raisin
Bread sticks

Cabbage
Cashews
Chestnuts
Chili powder
Collards
Cowpeas
Cress
Curry powder
Corn muffins
Dried fruits

Apricot
Acorn squash

Barley
Beets
Black beans
Berries
Bran cereal
Bread, pita
Blueberries

Cantaloupe
Celery
Chick peas
Cloves
Corn
Cornmeal
Cucumber
Crackers

Dates

Endive
Falafel
Figs
Fig Newton
Garlic
Grapes
Guava
Hazelnuts
Hickory nuts
Kidney Beans
Kumquat
Orange peel
Lima Beans
Lotus root
Mangos
Miso
Mushrooms
Macaroni
Navy beans
Okra
Onion, green
Oatmeal cookies
Papaya
Parsnip
Peanuts
Pecans
Persimmon
Pinto beans
Popcorn
Pretzels
Pummelo
Plums

English muffins
Fenugreek
Filberts
Fruit, frozen
Gingerroot
Great Northern beans
Grapefruit
Hominy
Horseradish
Kiwi
Leeks
Lentils
Lime
Macadamia nuts
Marjoram
Mulberries
Mustard greens
Muffins
Noodles
Oatbran
Oranges

Paprika
Passion fruit
Pear
Pepper, ground
Pine nuts
Pistachio nuts
Poppy seeds
Prickly pear
Pumpkin
Papaya

Farina
Flax seeds
Fruit, canned
Gooseberries
Green beans
Grits
Horseradish
Kale
Kohlrabi
Lemon peel
Lettuce
Loganberries
Macaroni
Millet
Mung beans
Macaroons

Nutmeg
Oatmeal
Oregano

Parsley
Peach
Peas
Pepper, green
Pineapple
Plantain
Potato
Prunes
Polenta
Peaches

Pancakes	Prunes	Pasta
Potatoes, sweet	Quince	Quinoa
Radishes	Raisins	Raisins
Raspberries	Red beans	Refried beans
Rhubarb	Rice, white	Rice, brown
Rutabega	Rye flour	Rice, wild
Rolls		
Sage		
Salsify	Sapodilla	Sapote
Sauerkraut	Seaweed	Semolina
Sesame seeds	Shallots	Snow peas
Sorghum	Soursop	Soy flour
Soybeans	Soy meal	Soy milk
Spaghetti	Spaghetti squash	Split peas
Spinach	Squash	Strawberries
Succotash	Sunflower seeds	Sweet potato
Swiss chard	Stuffing	
Tabbouleh mix	Tahini	
Tamarind	Tangerine	Taro
Tarragon	Thyme	Tofu
Tomato	Triticale	Turmeric
Turnip	Turnip greens	Tortillas
Vanilla wafers		
Waffles		
Walnuts	Water chestnuts	Watercress
Wheat flour	Wheat germ	Wild rice
Yam		
Zucchini		

Fat Burning PM Foods

Abalone

Almonds

Anchovies

Antelope

Bacon

Bacon substitutes

Beef

Brains

Breakfast drinks

Beef jerky

Catfish

Cheese

Chicken

Cornish hen

Chicken substitutes

Chili

Chitterlings

Clams

Cottage cheese

Crab

Cream cheese

Custard

Cold cuts

Deli meats

Duck

Eel

Eggs

Egg substitutes

Fish

Gefilte fish

Giblets

Gizzards

Goat meat

Goose

Guinea hen

Haddock

Hake

Halibut

Ham

Hamburger

Herring

Hot dogs

Kidneys

Lamb

Liver

Lobster

Mackerel

Meat sticks

Meat substitute

Milk

Milk, reduced fat

Milk substitutes

Milk, skim

Monkfish	Mussels
Nuts	
Octopus	
Oysters	
Peanut butter	
Peanuts	Perch
Pigs feet	Pike
Pistachios	Pork
Pudding	
Quail	
Rabbit	Rockfish
Roe	
Sardines	
Sausage	Salmon
Sausage substitute	Scallops
Scrod	Sea Bass
Sea Trout	Shad
Shell fish	Shrimp
Smelt	Snails
Snapper	Sole
Sour cream	Soy milk
Squab	Squid
Sturgeon	Sashimi
Sweetbreads	Swordfish
Tempeh	Tofu
Tongue	Turkey
Trout	Tuna
Turbot	Vegetarian substitutes
Veal	Venison
Walnuts	Yellowtail
Whitefish	Whiting
Yogurt, frozen	Yogurt

Anytime Foods

Asparagus
Broccoli
Cabbage
Celery
Cucumbers
Zucchini
Tomatoes
Coffee, regular & decaf
Tea, herbal & regular
Diet hot chocolate
Lowfat Rice Drink
Beef, Chicken or Vegetable broth
Reduced fat salad dressings
Nonfat cooking spray
Dill
Basil
Protein bars
Sugar free gum
One butterscotch hard candy
Artificial sweeteners

Bokchoy
Onion
Lettuce
Onion
Peppers
Garlic
Artichokes, fresh
Lettuce
Water
Lowfat Soy Drink
Diet soda
Consommé
Mushrooms
Parsley
Rosemary
Tarragon
Sugar free Popsicles
1 stick licorice
5 jelly beans
Stevia

Extra Fat Burning Impact Foods

Hot sauce
Tabasco
Horseradish
Vinegar
Garlic
Pepper
Pickled ginger
Nutmeg

Salsa
Mustard
Hot peppers
Curry powder
Onion
Wasabi
Allspice
Chili powder

Foods To Avoid

Sugar
Frozen fruit bars
Candy
Carrots
Orange juice
Ketchup
Sour Cream
Vegetable oils
Deep fried foods
Plum sauce
Croissants
Cream

Donuts
Candy bars
Salt
Bananas
Fruit juices
Mayonnaise
Alcohol
Lard
Full fat dairy products
High salt soy sauce
Scones
Half & Half

Information

To order Edita's Skinny Pills or Books:

Call toll free 1-888-7-SKINNY

Or visit www.skinny.com

Customer Service Contact:

1-888-7-SKINNY or email customerservice@skinny.com

To become a Distributor of Edita's Products

Call toll free 1-888-7-SKINNY

Or visit www.skinny.com or www.EditasBest.us

Write to:

Edita Kaye
Fountain of Youth Group, LLC
Skinny
830-13 A1A North
Ponte Vedra Beach, FL 32082

Corporate Offices: 904-273-3961
Fax Orders to: 1-904-280-9253